Hotel at the Edge of the World

Hotel at the Edge of the World

D.P. Gee

To
Mark O'Shea Gordon

First published in 1989 by
Brandon Book Publishers Ltd
Dingle, Co. Kerry, Ireland

ISBN: 0 86322 105 X

Cover design by Graphiconies, Dublin
Author photograph by the Elaine David Studio
Typeset by Irish Typesetting and Publishing Co. Ltd, Galway
Printed in Great Britain by
Richard Clay Ltd, Bungay, Suffolk

One

THE SONOROUS NOTES of the chapel bell were muted, audible only to waiting ears. This state of affairs was occasioned by the lashing rain. Water sluiced down the gutters to be gurgled up in the half-blocked cast-iron grills that supposedly guarded the street drains set at intervals along the pot-holed roads. To say that the sky wept would be an understatement. The village of Ballythread on the north-west coast of Donegal was often subjected to such inclement weather. The prayers and protests of the population proved entirely ineffective in warding off the deluge; like liquid stair-rods the rain continued to pour upon it.

The centre of the village, and the hub of all business activity, was inappropriately named the "Diamond". Any resemblance between it and the treasured stone was so remote that it could only have been christened by a person suffering from hallucinations or emerging from the horrors caused by too liberally imbibing strong alcoholic beverages. It consisted of a large open area, tarmacked in parts and separated from the main road by a double stone wall filled with earth which some hopeful town planner had probably visualized as a flower bed but wherein some stunted bushes, blighted rose plants and myriad weeds struggled to survive amidst a litter of bottles, beer cans, potato crisp packets and, for good measure, a large collection of plastic containers. An elderly gentleman, stooped and bent, occasionally elected to play the role of good citizen and poked in a futile manner around the roots of these withered plants in a fruitless effort to revive them.

Behind this pathetic effort was a car park. Some of the vehicles there had for many years had no other home. Battered and rusted they lay forgotten, set in their now permanent positions, many with flat tyres, others chocked up on breeze blocks, their wheels completely missing and any chance of further movement unlikely. The sole claim to fame of the area was the newly erected public toilets. The condition of this amenity, however, had so deteriorated that even the horde of dogs that scampered around the town moved upwind of the malodorous structure, thence to cock their legs or squat with glazed expressions while they fouled the uneven pavement. At either end of this rubbish-strewn wasteland the Dock Inn and the Fisherman's Bar vied with each other for the trade that the fishing boats were wont to provide after a successful haul. This trade varied both as to quantity and quality in direct ratio to the value of the catch and, likewise, the maintenance of good order and tranquillity varied on a similar scale.

On the far side of the main road, looking out over this beauty spot, were lined the essential business premises of the village. The ladies' dress shop featured garments purchased from some long out of date catalogue yet proudly displayed on cracked models posing behind the salt-spray-encrusted windows. A grocery shop stocked a wide variety of ancillary items in addition to foodstuffs and was run by a gentleman of benign disposition who stayed open far into the night, still managing to open in time to distribute the morning papers when they arrived on the bus from Donegal Town. There was a café-cum-fish and chip shop, full of bright modern plastic furniture and with a juke-box which ensured that the place was much frequented by the younger inhabitants who consumed innumerable burgers, bags of piping-hot chips and countless bottles of various mineral waters while listening with fascination to the twanging of guitars, or the howls and screams which unsuccessfully attempted tuneful harmony through the massive amplification of the machine. As luck would have it this emporium of youthful conviviality was separated from the other buildings by a disused garage, so the continual noise did not unduly disturb more sensitive souls.

Except for a narrow-fronted dwelling house occupied by a very old and very deaf lady, the remainder of the frontage of the Diamond was dominated by the Pier Gate Hotel. This venerable structure was reputed to have been constructed when Nelson was in knee pants, and many and varied alterations to its configuration at the whim of its various owners down through the years had resulted in a conglomeration of interconnected passageways, some leading to rooms and attic spaces of vast age, and some to more modern accommodation, but all constructed with no thought either to the past or of the future needs and requirements of the space enclosed behind the original massively thick stone walls. The hotel's reception area was provided with a large plate-glass window through which the full beauty of the Diamond could be surveyed. Beyond that the rusted cylindrical oil tanks with the adjoining lubricating oil store, and the high square tower of the ice production plant interrupted what might otherwise have been a wonderful viewpoint from which to survey the magnificent harbour and the boats that bobbed gently against the wooden pilings and fenders of the pier.

It was through this window that I now peered with a feeling of trepidation. Ballythread was the birthplace of my wife; indeed, it was within the walls of the Pier Gate that she had actually first entered the world. Though we had met and married in the warmer climes of the Channel Islands we had spent part of our honeymoon here, and frequent holidays. Even the birth of Ann and Elizabeth, our twin daughters, had not prevented our annual pilgrimage to this forsaken spot. But those visits had been different, for we had been fêted during our holidays and secure in the knowledge that a comfortable home and profitable occupation awaited our return. We had been able to enjoy the amenities of the hotel to the full and, being an ex-master mariner, I had found the company of the fishing fraternity both congenial and enjoyable. Now, however, as I squinted through the window at the lashing rain, I was far from sure that I had made the right decision when the opportunity had arisen for us to take over the hotel upon the retirement of my wife's mother. I would have to find out the hard way whether the friendship shown by the population during our holidays would continue now that we had taken up permanent residence in the town and, more to the point, the hotel.

My soliloquy was interrupted by the arrival of an elderly, brightly attired gentleman, who came up and stood behind me and likewise peered with gloomy fascination at the rivers of water running down the sheet of glass. The casual observer might well have been inclined to deduce that he had made a mistake in his location: his multicoloured cap was pulled firmly down on his forehead and his violently coloured shirt depicted scenes of surfing, sailing and nubile young ladies reclining under a profusion of tropical palm trees. This enchanting ensemble would have been more suited to the warmer temperature of the Caribbean or a leisurely holiday on some far-flung Pacific island paradise. He swayed gently as he focused his gaze through the waterlogged pane, and the aroma of Irish whiskey wafted from him at each exhalation of breath.

Being completely new to the hotel business I deduced that it was he who had been described to me as "the Yank in fourteen". I smiled tentatively at him, feeling that I must immediately start to play the part of host.

"God damn!" he announced. "Must be the cleanest trash-heap in the whole of Ireland – I've been here over a week now and I ain't never seen the dust rise."

Having absorbed this sentiment I felt it incumbent upon me to make some sort of defence of the place.

"It might clear up this afternoon," I ventured.

The American looked at me more in sorrow than in anger. "Is that what they told you, boy?" he spluttered. "The sons of bitches have been saying that for a full seven days, but so far the only place the water hasn't run is through the faucet in my bedroom. Why, I've been coming here now for a full six consecutive years and that faucet has been as dry as a witch's tit. Even the bar don't have no water sometimes. Then they tell you that if the whiskey was meant to have water in it the makers would have put it in the bottle – and as for ice! I've stopped asking for it. They look at you as if you're some kind of creature from outer space."

He paused for breath and I became intrigued.

"If you hate it so much how is it that you've been coming here for so long?"

"Got to," he moaned. "Was born here some sixty-seven years ago, and if I don't come over here and visit all the relations each year my name is crap. Jesus! They breed like rabbits, more of them every time I come, and they all try so hard to make me feel welcome. I tell you, boy, by the time I leave here I got a hangover that lasts the full year till the next time I come."

I chuckled at his vexation, and the hard lines of his face relaxed into a smile.

"Suppose I like it really," he admitted.

Our chat was interrupted by the arrival of a tall girl. She was clad in the wrap-over uniform of a housekeeper. Normally I would have classed her as attractive, with flashing brown eyes and beautifully moulded bone structure, but now she was flushed with annoyance and she strutted towards us with the step of an irate Sergeant Major.

I racked my brains. So many of the local populace seemed to have the same surname that I had found it difficult to place each member of the staff. It came to me: Paula Gillespie and, indeed, she was the housekeeper.

"Hello, Lady Paula," I said, trying to keep my tone light and friendly.

"He's been at it again," she snarled. "I'm just about fed up with it. If I find out who it is I swear he'll rue the day!"

"Not me, honey," said the American. "The brown bread that you serve over here binds me up so much that I couldn't do it even if I tried."

She cast such a withering look upon him that even his verbosity was stilled. "I know it isn't you, Jo," she snapped, "or I'd clear it with your skull."

"Lovely girl," he murmured, then resumed peering through the window with rapt attention lest worse befall him.

"What's the problem?" I enquired, trying to appear efficient and proprietorial.

"It's the phantom shitter!" she cried. "This time it's the one in the high end – blocked solid it is."

My brain reeled. Deductive ability failed, and so I gazed hopefully at the squat American, hoping that in some way he might solve the riddle.

"You got yourself a nut," he announced. "Some bum jams the toilet roll down the john, gives with the action – and boy! He's some heavy feeder. Then he flushes the son of a bitch and makes his exit laughing." He paused. "Never take my breakfast if he's beaten me to it."

My brain spun upon receipt of the explanation that he had so clearly defined, and it was obvious from the expression on the Lady Paula's face that I was expected to produce an immediate solution to the problem.

"Ho!" I intoned. "I'll have to do something about it."

"Indeed, that you will," she agreed. "For with the cistern leaking all the time like it does you'll soon meet the lot coming down the stairs towards you."

During my long and varied career do-it-yourself had never been one of my strong points, and such dread calamities as this had always been solved by an immediate and hysterical phone call to the local plumber. However, even with my slight knowledge of the Irish way of life I knew instinctively that this recourse would not be the answer. My previous dreams of the life of a hotel proprietor were roughly shattered. Thoughts of skilled chefs labouring with loving care over a selection of choice viands and my wants being attended to by a succession of scampering waitresses vanished out of the window. Here was a sticky problem, and I had apparently been elected to solve it.

Reluctantly I followed the housekeeper up the first flight of stairs, along the dark landing, up another flight and then puffed my way along a seemingly endless corridor until she arrived at a door. With an artistic flourish she pulled it open, then stood aside in order that I might view the offending convenience. My pre-formed mental definition of the problem proved all too correct, and a slight hissing noise from the cistern indicated that her own observation on the subject was also completely right; immediate action was required to avert a major overflow, the consequences of which were too awful to contemplate.

Some erudite ancient once propounded the theory that there was nothing like the imminent prospect of death to sharpen the intellect. I too had generally found that desperate occurrences had been resolved by sudden flashes of pure brilliance and, here again, such mental agility came to my assistance. "No problem," I said confidently. "Hang around and I'll get a five iron." I scurried off down the corridor, feeling the uncomprehending glare of the Lady Paula's eyes burning twin holes in my back.

I hurried to my private room, rummaged behind a mountain of suitcases and upon locating my golf bag extracted a five iron from it. Though never having been particularly effective on a golf course as, indeed, the remainder of my equipment, it had nevertheless performed many useful functions, such as curing an itch in a particularly inaccessible portion of my back or extracting a wide variety of small toys from beneath items of kitchen equipment or heavy furniture. In this instance I felt that it might well prove its true worth. Triumphant, I returned to the waiting housekeeper.

She looked at me scathingly. "Did you forget to bring your balls then?" she enquired in an acid tone.

Manfully I refrained from making the obvious answer and thrust the gleaming steel shaft into the fetid depths of the white porcelain. The American's forecast as to the hidden obstruction was immediately proven, and a deft twist and a jerk was rewarded by an ugly gurgling noise and the water level rapidly fell. An extra flush and the problem was solved.

The Lady Paula looked at me with what I hoped was a new respect shining from her eyes. "Well, well! That's clever, now," she said.

"I've an old club somewhere," I said. "I'll put it in your pantry; then, if this should happen again and I'm not around, you'll be able to save the day."

She nodded agreement at this profound sentiment and I made my exit making a mental note that should it happen

11

again I should make every effort to be well clear of the immediate vicinity.

When I returned to Reception Jo was still standing, hands clasped behind him, peering out of the window. My prognosis of an impending clearance seemed to be coming true, for an insignificant drizzle had replaced the former downpour.

"Didn't realize you were the new boss," he said. "Cops looking for you over there, or are you some kind of masochist?"

"Well, the cops aren't looking for me," I said, "but I'm beginning to wonder about the other. Is it always like this, or have I struck a bad day?"

The American beamed in jovial fashion. "Son, you've got a lot to learn. A joint like this makes a fruit-cake look positively sane. I get free beer for the whole year at home from the stories I tell about what goes on in this place, and they ain't bullshit, they're as true as I'm standing here."

He promptly sat on a convenient settee. "Brought my son, Jo junior, over here once," he volunteered. "He's a cop, one of New York's finest, a real harness bull. Works the Bowery and around South Ferry. He gets every type of crap that's going, has to break up fights all the time, and the whole area is arse high with lushes sleeping it off. He was here two weeks and his hand shook so bad he could stir a cup of coffee without even trying to. Said that when he got back to the States he was going to tell all the bums and lushes on his beat that they hadn't even learned to drink." He paused and shook his head sadly. "Wouldn't come over with me this time, said his guts wouldn't stand it. They don't breed 'em now like they used to."

"He must be a tough lad to hold down a job like that," I replied.

"Bull!" he exclaimed. "Compared to some of the characters that are running loose round this town he's like a babe in arms."

Much as I would have liked to remain with him and listen to more of his reminiscences I felt it incumbent upon me to appear as if I were busy, so I bade the elderly Yank farewell and popped my head into the bar.

This was strictly the domain of the redoubtable Ann Marie,

12

a lady of indeterminable age, who had ruled behind and in front of the counter for over forty years. Many of the locals supported the proposition that she also had uttered the immortal words "Kiss me Hardy" at the same time as Nelson. Though this was undoubtedly an exaggeration, she was able to recount events that had occurred in the Pier Gate before I was even a twinkle in my father's eye. It seemed most improbable, having due regard to her occupation and the length of her service, but not so much as one sip of alcoholic beverage had passed her lips since the day of her birth and, what is more, she had no intention of changing this state of affairs. Another of her claims to fame was her memory for various family trees. She was able to inform anyone what relation one person of the locality was to another, even though on many occasions the relationship was so tenuous that the persons enquiring were not aware that they were related at all.

At this moment she was wagging a short, stumpy index finger in admonition at a dishevelled middle-aged man who, by making a supreme effort, was managing to stand in front of the bar, though somewhat unsteadily.

"Would you look at this cockroach, sir," she chortled happily as I appeared.

"Just one wee half, Ann Marie," pleaded the supplicant.

"You'll get no more drink." She wagged the finger again to add emphasis to the pronouncement. "I'll give you a half pint of beer, but no more."

"And a wee half," wheedled the wretch.

Ann Marie sighed deeply and looked upon him more in sorrow than in anger.

"James McGonagle," she muttered. "If you don't stop annoying my head, I'll tell your mother."

The middle-aged man reeled back from the bar and slumped onto a stool as though struck by a bolt of lightning.

"You'd never do a thing like that, Ann Marie," he slurred. "It would be a sin to worry the poor old lady so. I'll just take the beer and be on my way."

Reluctantly she poured the beverage and placed it before him. He fumbled in his trouser pocket and slapped a handful of change on the highly polished counter, letting several coins and a filthy handkerchief fall to the floor in the process.

I made to pick them up, but Ann Marie stopped me. "Leave them be, sir," she exclaimed. "I'll put them in Father Burns's box when I sweep up. He'll put them to far better use than this creature should he get his paws on them again."

On many previous occasions when on holiday I had noticed that what I at first took to be dispenser units placed at regular intervals on top of the counter were actually a collection of donation boxes, all for good causes but predominated by subscription boxes for various religious organizations. Ann Marie supported each and every one by placing the coins swept from the floor into each box in strict rotation.

Now she smiled sweetly. "He's not such a bad man really; comes from Weeling, same as meself. The Bradeys and the McGonagles have lived there for years. I'll poke some soup and bread down the creature when I get the time and he'll be as right as rain."

It appeared that she had everything under control, and the remainder of the patrons were sitting in an orderly manner, gazing at their different libations with a reverence usually reserved for persons making their first inspection of the Holy Grail.

During the few days that had elapsed since I had arrived at the hotel to take over the proprietorship I had been aware that the staff had been sizing me up, in much the same manner as I had been doing to them. Ann Marie, however, was slightly different from the other, much younger women. Though she had said nothing and, indeed, her vast knowledge of the trade had been freely given to me, I had the distinct impression that she felt that my presence in her bar, though inevitable, was not particularly welcome. She obviously regarded any help or suggestion from me as an admonition that she was not doing her job to my satisfaction, and I felt that she would far rather have me outside the counter taking a jar than inside serving one. She had confided: "I has me own way of working." And after the scores of years that she had been behind the same bar I realized that she had no intention of changing it.

She bustled away to service the needs of some other parched devil and so, slightly at a loose end, I made my way into the kitchen.

Before I arrived at the hotel I had a very definite idea fixed in my mind as to the general appearance of the cook. I realized that much of the reputation of the hotel, and the smooth running of same, rested upon her shoulders. I had visualized a large, middle-aged woman of dictatorial disposition presiding over a hive of activity and tongue-lashing scurrying minions into an ever greater frenzy of various labours. This illusion had been most pleasantly shattered when I had been introduced to Catch Docherty.

Catch was a stunning blonde with long hair that hung in a silken sheen half-way down her back. Scarcely out of her teens, she ruled her domain with calm efficiency. How she had settled upon cooking for a livelihood was a mystery. One would have thought that she would have been more suited to gracing the front row of a chorus line, or wriggling and twirling down a catwalk showing off the latest creations of some exotic fashion house. So attractive was she that I still bore traces of a bruise on my shin which I received after remarking to my wife that "she has the bloom of youth in her cheeks, and the cheeks of youth in her bloomers".

When I entered the kitchen steam was hissing from the lids of various pots and pans; an appetizing aroma wafted from the large ovens and pervaded the area, defying the efforts of a large extractor fan to banish them. Evidently the lunch-time rush had not yet begun for Catch and Tat – my ever-loved wife – were perched upon the preparation table, drawing deeply on cigarettes and chattering gaily.

My wife was not, of course, baptized with the name of Tat. This pseudonym had been bestowed upon her by no lesser person than myself. During the heady days of our courtship I had mentally ascribed to her the lovable attributes of a small kitten: soft and cuddlesome, delightful to behold, and even more satisfying to stroke and make a fuss of. In my besotted state logic had deserted me and never did I think of the inescapable fact that kittens, the most amiable of small animals, would in the fullness of time develop into full-blown cats, these creatures being almost a different species, spitting and clawing until they achieved their own way and showing scant regard, even contempt, towards any hand that fed them.

"What have you been doing?" she asked.

Her tone of voice was accusing, as though convinced in her own mind that the answer must be the inevitable – nothing.

"I've just finished clearing a badly blocked toilet for the Lady Paula," I answered with a touch of triumph in my voice.

"Good enough for you – it's about time that the girls had a man that they could call upon to do little jobs like that for them."

This welcome for the hero of the toilet saga was far short of what I had expected, and I shuffled my feet indecisively. The two women looked at me enquiringly.

"I think I'll go for a pint," I ventured.

My ever-loving beamed at the cook with an expression of complete vindication on her face. "There," she said. "What did I tell you – as soon as it's liable to get busy you can always rely on a man to disappear to the pub."

"I'll stay and help if you want me to," I replied defensively.

"No, no," she sighed. "You'd only be in the way. Go and get your hand round a glass – at least you'll be doing something that you're well practised at."

Catch laughed heartily, apparently enjoying my discomfort. "It's probably a good idea anyway," she said. "What with the Mission in the town he'd probably say something to upset the Fathers if he stayed around."

I had rapidly found out that in this predominantly Catholic society my agnostic proclivities were viewed with complete disbelief, if not with some degree of suspicion; my eventual fate at the termination of life was considered too horrible to describe. I dreaded further conversation between the two women on this particular subject and so made a rapid exit, followed by the amused smiles of a few waitresses and the wash-up girl, all of whom were sitting at a table in the upper kitchen. The drizzle had temporarily ceased so I stepped outside onto the wet pavement.

Two

THE MISSION ARRIVED in Ballythread approxima-
tely every four years and while it stayed the inhabitants were subjected to a continual barrage of religious
instruction, the church bells tolling regularly to summon the
faithful to listen to the fervent exhortations of the Mission
Fathers, as with sheer verbosity and volume they sought to
purge the population of accumulated sin and teach them the
path of true righteousness. Surprisingly, the residents viewed
their aggressive approach with complete equanimity, as
though the injunction that they were all sinners in need of
salvation was only to be expected. Likewise, the atmosphere
in the town during this week of religious fervour was more
akin to that of a carnival than to it having any lasting effect on
their life styles.

The movements of the Mission Fathers from place to place
were closely followed by a motley band of travelling salesmen
and their spouses. With scant regard for the convenience of

17

the townspeople or the amenities of the village, they set up their wood and canvas stalls where they caused the maximum disruption to the flow of traffic. Within these makeshift shops were displayed collections of holy items. Large statues of the King of Kings, china and metal crosses in various designs and colours, racks of holy beads, shelves of plastic bottles reputed to contain holy water from the shrines at Lourdes or – nearer to home – from Knock, large selections of plastic fonts wherein this water could conveniently be poured, and a profusion of brightly coloured statues of the Blessed Virgin, all of which were supposed to be placed in the homes of the faithful to guard them against sin during the intervening time before the next Mission arrived. All these wonders were available for purchase at exorbitant prices and in the main discreetly bore the stamp – *Made in Birmingham*. These holy relics were avidly snatched up by the populace, probably on the theory that having bought one the purchaser was thereby absolved from having to attend each and every Mass and lecture that the missionary priests performed during their stay.

I had parked my car between two of these stalls and, flushed with pleasure over my comparatively easy escape from the hotel, I crossed the road towards it, trying to make up my mind which of the local hostelries should have the delight of benefiting from my custom. I decided on a small inn some two miles down the road called the Holly Leaf. Here, any person sorely afflicted with the dreaded thirst was assured of a warm welcome from the proprietor and his attractive wife. It was also a popular watering place for the numerous farmers in the area, a very friendly band of men, though much of their conversation concerned ewes and the like of "I had a bull to serve her only this morning". After a short while of listening to such postulations one was moved to contemplate the exotic advantages of reincarnation wherein one might be returned to earth in the form of a stud bull.

Passing the stalls I felt slightly guilty for not pausing to admire the proliferation of religious statues set out on display, and hastily jumped into the car. My lack of enthusiasm had apparently not been noticed and with a sigh of relief I turned the key and heard the powerful engine roar into life. Peering

18

steadfastly ahead I let in the clutch. This was my first mistake, for when I had backed the vehicle into the space I had neglected to remove the gear lever from reverse. My second mistake was in not checking this fact before letting in the clutch. The car shot backwards with me hanging on to the steering wheel like a rabbit hypnotized by a snake. A grinding crash announced my arrival at an unknown destination, and luckily the engine cut out.

Trying to maintain some semblance of dignity, I climbed out of the machine. My ears were assailed by a sound that could only be likened to that of a banshee having its toes trodden on by an elephant. It transpired that this sound emanated from an ancient crone wrapped in a plaid rug, whose mission in life was to persuade the passing throng to purchase from the stall that I had inadvertently backed into.

"Lord save us!" she howled at a decible count that I would have thought impossible for the human voice to achieve. "It's an earthquake!"

I looked into the stall with mounting anxiety. The impact had done nothing to improve the display; in fact, the flimsy structure had been shaken to its foundations. Most of the precious stock had fallen from the makeshift shelves and lay in heaps of broken china on the ground. Never in my life had I seen so many virgins spread out before me. As I pondered what to do an old man appeared at a half trot. Purple with fury, he seemed on the verge of apoplexy.

"You'll have to pay for all this!" he roared.

The ever-expanding circle of onlookers nodded their agreement to this statement, and I began to feel like a trapped animal facing its doom. Mustering what little reason I had left I waved my hand in all-embracing fashion. "Of course," I agreed wholeheartedly. "I'm from the hotel across the street. You make out the bill and come and see me this afternoon."

My acquiescence mollified the old man and he went to comfort the haggard crone who, having discovered that it was not an act of God but an act of man that had caused the disaster, had ceased to howl and now stood glaring at me with malevolent eyes. It occurred to me that this was an excellent time to make my exit, so with a false and jaunty smile at the onlookers, disappointed that the impromptu theatre had stopped, I attempted to climb nonchalantly into the car and, as the throng parted, I drove away.

The Holly Leaf appeared in front of me like an oasis to a desert traveller, and I braked to a halt in front of the door. As I entered the hum of conversation dried up and heads moved together as one member of the company explained to the remainder as to who I was and from whence I came.

"It's the Englishman from the Pier Gate," I heard in hushed whispers.

This fact having been established and digested the conversations proceeded normally and Vera, the wife of the proprietor, came over and asked my pleasure. The thought crossed my mind that a pint of arsenic might well be the best choice, thus ending all my woes, but against this judgement I opted for a black wine of the country. Vera moved the pump handle with dexterity and precision, allowing the black liquid first to fill half the glass, then, after a short rest, slowly added to it, causing the white head to appear and float upon the surface. I realized that I was watching the perfect pint being prepared, so I possessed my soul in patience till the performance was completed and the glass was placed in front of me.

The first sip of the Guinness made my journey worthwhile, though if truth be told I could not have looked a particularly happy customer, hunched over the glass and feeling a deep gloom pervade my system. I brooded, wondering what effect my unfortunate accident would have between the local people and myself, bearing in mind that a good and friendly relationship was essential if the hotel was to continue to prosper. Then there was Tat. What she would think and, more to the point, say was beyond my comprehension, but judging from the fact that both she and Catch had deemed it advisable for me to be out of town because something I might unknowingly say would offend the Fathers, well, when she heard that I had wrecked a religious stall ...

I had not long to wait before the first reference to my misfortune was forthcoming. I had scarcely worked my way through half of the pint when the door opened and, with a loud clanking of milk bottles, Charlie Byrne the local milkman appeared. Once again the conversation hushed as the new

20

arrival was scrutinized by the incumbents. It was Charlie who broke the silence. Looking directly at me, and with an impish grin of delight on his face, he pronounced, "I wasn't coming in for a drink today boys but, when I saw the holy car outside, well, I thought it must be a signal from above." He approached the bar and stood beside me. "Here, Vera. Set up a wee half of Bush and give this gentleman his pleasure, for I'm sure that his need is greater than mine."

A chorus of voices called out to enquire the meaning of his message and, after sipping on the amber liquid placed in front of him, he proceeded to recount in great detail the disaster that had befallen me. I began to wish that the floor would open, and visions of lynch-mobs ran through my mind. It was therefore with a feeling of relief and wonder that I heard first a titter, then a laugh, then, as Charlie continued to elaborate, howls of glee. The assembled drinkers rocked in their chairs with merriment, glasses were banged on the table tops to show extra appreciation, and half-choked comments floated back.

"What's his name: would it be Cromwell?"

"The Fathers will choke on their soup!"

"Give the poor fella a wee half, Vera."

It appeared that I had suddenly become a firm favourite of the assembly, and conviviality seemed to be the order of the day. Hardened figures that I had previously only known by sight, redolent with the smell of the byre, beat me on the back in jovial fashion and invited me to sup up. Consequently it was with some degree of alcoholic euphoria that I finally tore myself away from the company and drove carefully back to the village, taking special care to park outside the hotel and well away from the stalls.

Since my slightly inebriated state would have been immediately noticed by Tat, who was possessed with the eyes of a hawk, it was advisable to steer well clear of further agony, and so I headed for my office. The christening of such a pokey little cubby-hole with the grandiose title of "office" was a misnomer, but the very smallness of the glorified cupboard had many advantages: one, that when I was seated in the comfortable chair that it boasted, nobody else could possibly get in; and, two, that when the door was closed it was impossible for any person to know with certainty whether I was in or out. Likewise, for working purposes all was conveniently at hand and I had only to swing the chair around and all the forms, papers, etc., were racked in neat piles on the shelves behind me. I had no trouble mastering the complexities of a filing system since the previous proprietor had deemed the provision of such luxuries unnecessary and had tipped all into large cardboard whiskey boxes. I was to find in the future that this system, though not being at all efficient, had certain advantages since, taking into account the temperament of the Irish, they were perfectly prepared to wait for weeks if the logical explanation that I was searching the files for their account was propounded.

I sat contentedly in the comfort of the chair, feeling my eyes slowly closing and my head nodding forward as the urge for sleep overcame me, when there was a knock on the door. I pulled myself together and opened it, trying to look the picture of efficiency. It was the old man from the holy stalls, a firm and determined expression on his face and a sheet of paper torn from a notebook clutched in his hand.

"This is what you did," he snarled, thrusting the rather grubby piece of paper under my nose.

I read through it with mounting disbelief and rapidly became aware that I was in the presence of what in Ireland was known as a "good business man". In other words, you couldn't trust him as far as you could throw a well-built elephant.

Cataclysms had befallen the earth since early times, and it appeared that my small accident could have been listed under this heading. The list read:

DAMMIGES

King of Kings (8)	@ £8.00	=	£64.00
Pictures of Our Lord's Heart (5)	@ £3.20	=	£16.00
Holy Mottos (6)	@ £3.00	=	£18.00
Blessed Virgin Statues (7)	@ £6.00	=	£42.00
Small China Statues (15)	@ £3.00	=	£45.00
Plastic Fonts (14)	@ £1.50	=	£21.00
Repairs to Stall Door		=	£10.00
TOTAL:		=	£216.00

I perused this itemized statement, trying to keep my face as straight as possible, but as I looked my mind was racing. Once again, under the pressure of the occasion, a solution flashed into my brain.

"That seems fair enough," I said, smiling with false geniality at the man, "but I thought that at least you would have charged me at the wholesale price?"

"Couldn't do that," he snarled. "I would have sold all of them, and I'd be doing without my profit if I charged you that."

I smiled happily again. "Well, it doesn't really matter, because I can write off all the Value Added Tax, and that won't make it so hard on me."

I paused, and then asked innocently. "Of course, you are registered for Value Added Tax?"

His feet shuffled and the eyes that had been so fierce only a few moments ago suddenly refused to look at me. I decided to rub it in a bit.

"It doesn't really matter to me if you aren't," I said. "The Tax Inspector in Letterkenny, Joey McClusky, is a personal friend of mine. I'll just get on the phone and he'll be able to issue you with a number right away, and then you can do all the rest of the details at any time that it is convenient to you."

The old man appeared to deflate rapidly. He gazed at the ceiling, scuffed his shoes on the floor and looked as if he were awaiting guidance from above. "Maybe the woman made a mistake," he said finally.

"I think she might have done," I said. "Maybe she put the breakages in a box with things that were broken already, and probably she neglected to tell you. Why don't you go over and check, then we can get on to Letterkenny and get the whole unfortunate affair cleared up."

He made no reply but turned rapidly and scampered off down the stairs.

I sat in the chair ruminating on the various aspects of the affair and working out which way I would play it, all depending on what he would do. My meditation was interrupted by his return.

"Now sir," he half moaned. "To be sure, isn't it you that were right. She did indeed put them all into the box where we keep damaged items."

"How much?" I enquired.

He agonized again, screwing up his cap in his hands as he did so. "Twenty pounds, sir, should see me right," he finally managed to enunciate.

I reached into my wallet and proffered a ten pound note.

"That's more like it," I said. "I'll send the hotel handyman over to you and he'll fix the door at my expense, so we're all square."

He accepted the note, though he seemed close to tears, but I smiled happily at him as if the settlement has been mutually agreed.

He shuffled his feet again and showed no inclination to depart. "You'll not be wanting the Value Added Tax back on just such a few pounds?" he enquired plaintively.

"No, no," I assured him. "It really wouldn't be worth the bother."

He placed his cap firmly on his head and looked at me with an ingratiating stare. "Then I'll thank you very much, sir. It's a pleasure to do business with a man that pays his just debts with such good grace."

He sidled out of the office, and once again I settled myself comfortably in the chair and prepared to let the balm of rest overcome me.

During my perambulations round the village in the succeeding days I was surprised to find that a definitely warmer feeling towards the newcomer was emanating from the local populace. It appeared that my exploit with the Mission stall had caused much hilarity, and had apparently lost nothing in the telling and re-telling as the story was promulgated. Collections of very hardy looking fishermen absorbing their daily intake of the black stuff in the various pubs that I entered made it obvious that I was welcome to join their company, and on several occasions I was requested to adjudicate between two protagonists hotly arguing over the finer points of Maritime Law, and my words of wisdom on the subject were treated with a certain respect. Naturally my beloved Tat had made it her business to aquaint herself with all the facts of the incident but even she did not push the subject too hard and was well pleased when I described the outcome. But the final seal of approval of my new-found acceptance by the community was stamped by the guardian of local law and order.

Three

I N BALLYTHREAD THE majesty of the law, and in
many cases the official strictures imposed by the authorities, were made manifest in the form of the Sergeant of the
Garda. This gentleman was what was colloquially known as
"a fine figure of a man". He tipped the scales at some twenty-
two and a half stones, and most of it was bone and muscle. He
spurned the use of the regulation blue uniform as a means of
imposing his authority and was to be seen, mostly after dark,
strolling through the streets of the village or with his ample
backside perched on the window-sill outside the Pier Gate, a
flat tweed cap pulled incongruously down over his bullet-like
head and his upper body swathed in a vast, white, cable-knit
Aran pullover, heavy blue trousers being his only concession
to his office. He later confided to me that "them young Gardas
go wearing their shoe leather out chasing all over the
countryside trying to apprehend villains, but I just sits here
and by and by they pass." This theory was apparently correct,

for on many occasions I watched him leap from the window-sill and lay a mighty hand on some wretch proceeding erratically across the Diamond.

A few days after my exploit I chanced to pass as he sat on his usual perch; until now he had acknowledged me with courtesy, but with no great degree of enthusiasm. This particular evening, however, he deliberately drew me into conversation and, inevitably, my *faux pas* came up. He related what he had heard, a very much embellished version of actuality. With great gusto, his ample frame heaving with mirth, he regaled me with a word-by-word account of what had transpired, as reported to him from his various sources. When he came to the arrangement of the settlement his jowels shook with appreciation and his face positively split with a grin of delight. "Ho, ho!" he snorted. "If only I'd been there to see it, it would have fair made my day. For all their holy relics that crowd are the biggest rogues ever to infest a man's patch but, be jeepers, they'll think more than twice before they try to play the mickey with you again."

Since our arrival my wife had attempted to acquaint me with the myriad propensities of the many prominent members of the village, and I was aware that the Sergeant was not averse to consuming a pint and a wee half-one at frequent intervals during his tour of duty in order to keep his bulk free from the terror of dehydration. In view of his present obvious good humour it seemed a good time to make an offer of hospitality, and it was with only a little trepidation that I suggested that we should adjourn to the hotel and slake our thirsts. My instinct in the matter had been faultless and he accepted with alacrity.

The bar was quite crowded but we managed to find two stools convenient to an empty table and I purchased the necessary glasses of liquid protein and calories. He proved an amusing raconteur, his first story concerning times long past when he had been appointed to Ballythread. With the common assumption of many Irish people in small communities he took it for granted that the names he mentioned would be well known to any person, whether they were acquainted with the area or not.

"I remember," he mused, "old Séamus Dock used to run a

donkey and cart from here up to his house in Lintra. Half of the time he was so full that the donkey used to see him home, him lying in the back of the cart. In them days I was new to the town and didn't have the know-how that I have now. I knew that he never had a light on the back of his cart, as is required by law, and so, one night, I lay in wait at the old bridge. I well knew that he would be coming along soon, but some person in the town must have told him what was awaiting him. By and by I heard the clatter of the donkey's hooves, and I knew that he was a-coming, so I braced myself. There was a silence and then the hooves started coming on again. There he was, and I shone my torch upon him."

He paused for breath and refreshment.

"'Ho!' I said. 'Séamus, you've no light on the back of the cart!'

"Then I looked again. Would you believe, the old bugger had taken the donkey out of the shafts and tied it on behind the cart, and he himself was between the shafts pulling the whole lot.

"'Ha!' he slurred. 'I figured that you might be standing here minding your own business, but, if there's no light on the back of the cart, then you'd better fine the driver.'"

He took a deep draft and, with a mournful expression on his face, set the glass down. "Well, what could you do in a case like that? After all, I'd have looked the bigger ass if I'd have brought a donkey to court!"

"Never mind," he consoled himself, "I learned fast. And the place seems to be ticking along quite well at this very minute."

I joined his own laughter at the story, and he then continued to recount many episodes in his long career. I replenished the glasses and he continued. However, after a while I noticed that he was spending more time looking over my shoulder than he spent looking at me as the stories poured from him.

"Look you," he muttered. "See the man at the corner of the bar: do you know him?"

I looked surreptitiously and replied in the negative. He was a well-dressed man in his early thirties; his grooming and general demeanour suggested that he might be a commercial traveller for some reputable company. However, he had on one side of him a highly painted, so-called "dolly bird", and on the other side a similar version, except that where the first was a peroxide blonde, this one boasted a head of long auburn hair, scarcely natural but also befitting her appearance. As the Sergeant and I watched in fascination the man attempted to attract both women at the same time. Judging from the way he behaved he was already well jarred, and he no doubt had visions of the endless delights that would be forthcoming later in the night. He set up expensive drinks for the two girls as though alcohol would soon be in short supply. They sucked upon the proffered beverages with the avidity of a thirsty camel after a long trip over the Sahara desert.

We continued watching as this courtship rolled on and, since watching is thirsty work, frequently refilled our own glasses. As the man casually rested his hand on the knee of one of these visions, so the other would whisper something in his ear, and he would turn his attention to her. This standard by-play seemed to go on *ad infinitum* and his calls for more liquid nourishment became more frequent. At last the witching hour came near and I was forced to nod to the barmaids that the time had come to close, for, though the law was still with us, I had never before encountered him in similar circumstances and was not sure of the form.

It was only then that the object of our attention came over and announced that he required accommodation for the night. I mentioned to a barmaid who was clearing a table near us that he wanted rooms, but she informed me that all we had left was one twin-bedded room in the high end. This uplifting piece of information was duly passed to the gentleman. The Sergeant and I rocked with silent merriment when, after a lengthy and slightly acrimonious discussion, it was decided between the trio that the two women would take the twin that was offered, but that their amiable provider of the night would sleep in the back seat of the car. Even I felt my heart go out to him, and I tentatively suggested that we would have no objection if he were to share the room with his companions and pay for the extra bed. The gentleman nearly danced with delight at being given such an opportunity and hastened back to his girlfriends to break the good news. Here, however, he met with a somewhat cooler reception than was deserved and was informed in no uncertain fashion that they "were not girls like that". It was no great tribute to his world-wise appearance that he accepted this explanation, though both the Sergeant and I had previously decided that, even if they were only playing a small game now, that was exactly what they were.

However, the decision had been made and they, as well as the remainder of the customers, slowly filtered away. The three protagonists lingered in the reception area until finally with great kisses both the ladies disappeared up the stairs and the object of their attention hied himself into the outer darkness, presumably to make the best of a bad job and compose himself to rest in the uncomfortable confines of the back seat of his car – there, no doubt, to ponder upon the vicissitudes of life and tease his imagination with what might have been.

The Sergeant was much amused by this exhibition and volunteered: "If the idiot is still hunched up in his motor car when I go out I'll give him a shake and let him have a bed in one of the cells".

He then showed his appreciation of the evening's entertainment by offering to purchase another round. Although well after the legal hour for the consumption of alcohol it was patently obvious that with the guardian of the law different rules applied, and so we were immediately attended to by Ann Marie, who seemed delighted that the big man had decided to grace the premises. The lights were turned out, and we moved to sit on high stools at the bar.

From then on I might as well not have been in the place at all. Ann Marie and the Sergeant started to exchange reminiscences of many a bygone year, talking about people that I had never even heard of but making the whole of the conversation semi-intelligible to a newcomer. Their anecdotes of past happenings, whether I knew of the persons concerned or not, would have made a cat laugh. Had I been in other circumstances I might have been forgiven for thinking that a scriptwriter was compiling a format for his next humorous television series, yet from the serious nature of the conversation I was made aware that the outlandish happenings related had at some time actually occurred and were obviously remembered by both.

I made a hazy mental note that I should collect all the anecdotes that I had heard and keep them for a later date. But by the time the big man wandered on his way my recollection of the details involved in each story was dimmed, not so much by the mass of information that had been forthcoming as by the volume of alcohol consumed during the telling. I bade good night to Ann Marie who, in her own inimitable and tireless fashion, had begun to wash the bar floor and polish all the tables, ready for the following day's activity. I climbed the stairs and carefully slid into my side of the bed so as not to awaken the sleeping beloved. In this I was successful and she slumbered peacefully on.

Four

THE FOLLOWING DAY dawned bright and clear for a pleasant change, and I feigned not to notice a distinct throb over the right temple. The standard remark of the drinking fraternity in such circumstances was, "as fine a day as you could wish for, if only you had the health to enjoy it". Luckily the activities of the morning soon cleared the cobwebs from my head, but it was with some relief that I heard Tat inform me that this was the day that my duties included driving some fifty miles to collect our daughters, Elizabeth and Ann, from their weekly boarding school which was situated through a gap in the mountains in a small country town. This particular job was the excuse that I had been waiting for, and I immediately made a rapid exit from the hotel and climbed into my vehicle.

Casting a malevolent look at where the Mission stalls had once perched, I set off, driving carefully over the pot-holed roads that connected the village of Ballythread with the remainder of Ireland. The roads further on were not much better, but I persevered, passing through the county town of Donegal. From then on the scenic views grew more magnificent; small secluded farms nestled amid the splendour of the mountains, though the masses of dark-grey granite indicated that the land was of very poor quality and the main income of the families living in their picture-book settings came from the possession of a few sheep, many of which roamed down the slopes and crossed the road with scant regard for the passing traffic. But at least, fast driving being out of the question, the full panoramic beauty of the area could be appreciated and enjoyed to the utmost.

In the middle of the gap which slashed between two of the mountains I passed a large and slightly peeling sign-board which demanded in no uncertain fashion that the passing traveller should "Stop at Breeda's". Never having been a driver who disobeyed the rules of the road I slowed right down and soon came upon a charming wayside inn, set well back from the road and looking for all the world as though it had stood there from time immemorial. Its sole claim to modernity was provided by a battered petrol pump set incongruously in front of the building but, except for a wisp of smoke from the chimney and the rich aroma of smouldering turf, the inn seemed lifeless.

I pulled in and parked at the far end of the lay-by, and emerged to stretch my legs and breathe deeply the clean, unpolluted air. Even though the gap provided a passage through the mountains it was still at quite an altitude and there was a brisk, chill bite to the slight breeze that rustled through the sparse clumps of grass. Many times during my holiday visits to the Emerald Isle I had made a mental note that I should always carry a camera with me but, like many of my good resolutions, I had never actually got around to doing anything about it, and this again was a time that I wished that I had done so. The splendour of the situation was such that any landscape artist who faithfully recorded it upon canvas would be accused of exaggeration and embellishment, and I meditated as to whether the much vaunted new technology in colour film could possibly record the actuality of such beauty.

Eventually I sauntered across the gravelled surface to the

thick, rough-hewn, timber door, secured by an ancient cast-iron latch still faithfully fastening the portal, as the person who had forged it possibly over a century ago had intended that it should. Here was no thrown-together modern workmanship but a door and a latch intended to last through the generations that were to follow, hanging on stout wooden frames set solidly into thick stone walls. Very little chance of the ice-cold, howling gales of winter penetrating this particular abode. I bore down on the latch and entered the establishment. The room was of sizeable proportions and no attempt had been made to conform to the trends of modern bar decor. The floor was of great granite flagstones, worn smooth with the passage of feet over the years, and a liberal supply of heavy wooden tables and chairs, the wood scrubbed and re-scrubbed to a pure white sheen, filled the room. In one corner was set a small bar, though the main feature of the place was a huge turf fire, glowing cherry red and radiating welcome. A pine dresser stood loaded with a variety of old plates and platters, jugs, cups and bowls that would have had an antique dealer drooling with envy. And, as if also part of the furnishings, an old lady sat warming herself in front of the fire.

She nodded politely when I entered but made no move to leave the warmth of the hearth. Instead she let out a stentorian bellow, impressive in volume and clarity for a person of her age.

"Marie!" The echo lingered on.

A fat girl bustled in through another door, a fine big agricultural girl. Her red cheeks were flushed with exertion and she looked at me enquiringly. I ordered a bottle of stout and she scampered behind the small counter, then placed the requested beverage together with a tall glass at one of the tables close to the fire. Having done so and accepted payment she returned from whence she had come.

The old lady relaxed somewhat and entered into conversation with the newcomer. Skilfully and pointedly she obtained the information that she wanted. Who? Where from? What did I do? Why was I here? In the space of five minutes she had practically obtained my life history, and upon hearing that I was residing in Ballythread she exuded charm.

"You be one of the lucky ones to be living there," she stated.

"Nothing I likes better than a bite of fresh fish for me tea, but out here we never see it at all at all."

I promised that on my next run through I would drop her in some, which information she accepted with no great faith, but when I had finished my drink she bade me a cheerful farewell and good luck to speed me on my way.

I reached the school without incident, and was once again struck by the Irish penchant for the unpredictable. The building, sited opposite a malodourous cattle market at the far end of the aged village, could have been placed in the most modern setting and not been amiss. I had arrived just in time, for, as I pulled to a halt in the car park, the main doors burst open and a variety of small figures tumbled forth like peas from a pod. Jostling and shouting my two forged a path towards me waving their satchels like clubs and leaping with excitement at the prospect of being released from their tutorial prison to run amok through Ballythread during the week-end. Breathlessly they flung themselves into the car and, except for a cursory "Hello Daddy", continued to chatter animatedly about some happening during their five-day incarceration in the boarding division of the school.

As I started the car and moved slowly down the driveway I gathered that the high point of the week had been provided by some young devil by the name of Peter, who had etched his name for evermore in the annals of the school by having been caught, not only in the girls' dormitory at night, but actually in one of the young ladies' beds, there presumably avidly pursuing his study of biology to a degree never contemplated by the master who taught that particular subject. Both his and the young lady's efforts in the pursuit of knowledge had not been looked upon favourably by the headmaster, and both had been summarily banished from the school, no doubt to suffer the wrath of their respective families and probably be the cause of a feud that would continue for generations, especially if the efforts of the said Peter and the fertility of the young lady were eventually found to have achieved the expected result. My own two little innocents viewed the whole affair with great hilarity and, but for the omnipotent presence of father, would no doubt have discussed the occurrence in far

34

greater detail. We thus proceeded to Ballythread in the best of humour.

The rapturous welcome usually given by Tat to her brood was formally evident, but I detected a slight difference to that given on the many previous occasions and, after the two girls had rushed upstairs to change into more congenial clothing than that of the school uniform, I enquired the reason for this less than usually effusive welcome. It transpired that while I had been away to rescue the twins news had come through that Mrs Moira Gull had passed peacefully away from this world. Since the said Moira had weathered some eighty summers and eighty winters this event had been expected for some time, but she had been a special friend of my Tat, especially during her youth and, as such, her demise was of more than usual concern.

"We'll have to go to the wake," Tat said.

The Irish custom of laying out the dead in the parlour so that all the friends and relatives can come and pay their last respects had always seemed to me to be a particularly callous way of sending the dear departed to their last resting place, especially for the nearest and closest of the family, and I viewed my appearance at the wake in a slightly jaundiced light. However, when I made a small protest that possibly the departed would not notice if I were not in attendance, I was forcibly informed by Tat that she was aware of that fact but that all the survivors of the clan would definitely notice my absence and I should henceforth be branded a heartless heathen who could not spare the time to demonstrate grief during this critical hour. My half-hearted protest that they all knew that I was a heathen was brushed aside, and I was left in no doubt that I should have to attire myself suitably and accompany herself on this pilgrimage. Consequently, after our now dirt-stained offspring had returned from their amusements in the village and had been duly admonished, bathed, powdered and settled in their beds for the night, I was also forced to wash, change into a suit of dark grey and, thus arrayed, was manoeuvered to the car.

Tat, clad now in a skirt instead of the usual jeans that she affected, settled herself in the seat beside me. I followed her directions as we wended our way into the countryside, and as the tyres rolled over increasingly poorly maintained roads I was subjected to a lecture as to how to conduct myself at such an affair. I gathered that intense grief was the order of the day, though, to the best of my knowledge, I had never met the poor lady.

"Don't tell any of your funny stories."

"Don't ask where she's going to be cremated."

"Don't tell them that they do it differently in England."

"They'll probably ask for a funeral lunch; if they do, pretend to be suprised but assure them that you will see to it personally and that it will be the finest that they could obtain, even if they went to Donegal Town, but don't appear too eager."

All these words of wisdom were ringing in my ears as we arrived in a particularly desolate part of the countryside, now graced with lines of expensive motor cars parked along the road outside of a small thatched cottage. I found a parking space and Tat leapt out enthusiastically. I followed her unwillingly towards the small building, attempting but failing miserably to avoid the deep, muddy puddles that surrounded the residence.

Theoretically it was an impossibility for the area of the cottage to hold the number of persons that it now contained within its four walls, but this was Ireland, and there they were. We managed to push our way into the smoke-filled room and were greeted by a middle-aged lady with red, tear-stained eyes. It transpired that she was the daughter, who had been living "across the water" for some twenty years and to the best of anybody's knowledge had not set foot in her homeland during all that time. She recited the standard litany of her delight that of all those present we were so considerate as to spare our valuable time to come all this way to show our respects to her dearly beloved mother. When I attempted to reply in my distinctly English accent she appeared slightly nonplussed, but immediately passed us on to her brother.

He was a fine-looking man in his late thirties and it later transpired that he, too, had spent many years across the water. His duties at present focused around a small table that was laden with every sort of alcoholic beverage known in the locality. His eyes were slightly glazed, but he gazed upon us with a deeply sympathetic expression. "After journeying all this way you must be famished," he said, trying to lock both eyes upon my wife. "Would you be taking a cup of tea, or would you feel in need of something stronger?"

"Maybe a small sherry would sit well?" he enquired, looking at me.

I nodded in what I sincerely hoped was a sufficiently gloomy manner. He turned, and we were then presented with two glasses each containing sufficient liquid to numb the average charging lion.

New arrivals took our place and we moved aside, carefully holding on to our drinks lest the longer-serving mourners would stumble into us and knock them out of our hands. It seemed the natural course of things that we should eventually pass by the coffin of the late Mrs Gull, who lay in ethereal splendour, completely oblivious to all the noise that was taking place around her. It crossed my mind that never, during her earthly life, had she been the focus of so much attention, and certainly never the cause of so much alcohol consumption. Already many of the mourners were becoming increasingly loquacious in their descriptions of the departed.

"Ah! She was a fine woman and will be greatly missed by us all," seemed to be a common sentiment.

"To be sure. Even though she lived away out here there was little she didn't know about the happenings in the district. Why, if a fly shit on a window within twenty miles of the place, she would be able to tell you before you arrived."

As the night wore on, not only was the deceased discussed amongst those present, but her various offspring also came in for their fair share of comment.

"Ah, yes! I remember Charlie. He's the one in America: couldn't manage to get home for this sad occasion. He must be doing well out there: he was always a bright one; he'd skin a bee for its hide if he thought there was a market for it."

My wife smiled and agreed with all these pronouncements and added extra information herself, and I would have felt completely out of the affair had it not been for the brother who assiduously circled the room filling the glasses of those dying of the thirst brought on by their intense grief. Several times he poured massive bumpers of whiskey into my glass, and I noticed that my usually abstemious wife always seemed to have an empty glass when the sherry bottle put in an appearance.

After several such replenishments it occurred to me that these wakes were perhaps not such a bad idea, and when the scratchy noise of an ancient fiddle emanated from the far side of the room it seemed to be a perfectly normal and natural progression in the sequence of events since we had arrived. Several lusty voices joined the chorus of the tune that the fiddler attempted, and the notes missing through ineptitude were more than made up for by the volume of the accompaniment. Though completely ignorant of the words of the various ballads I was much impressed by the dulcet tones and the harmonious rendering of many of them by one particular member of the company until I realized, with some degree of apprehension, that the beautiful rendition was being produced by myself. However, the beaming faces all around had obviously not been offended by my efforts; in fact, the brother attended to the state of my glass at even more frequent intervals and I noticed that my beloved Tat, whose vocal accomplishments she admitted were far inferior to my own, was also joining in the general cacophony of musical talent.

At some stage of the night I was informed by a now close friend, who was helping me to support the wall, that it was customary for the deceased to be attended till the morning, and with a great effort I tried to regain what little senses I still had remaining. Lifting my feet high to circumnavigate imaginary obstacles, I made my way towards my beloved. She was comparatively easy to find since she had one buttock perched on a table and was emitting a noise that could only be reproduced by a tom-cat that had its balls caught in a mangle. The fiddler was responding to her efforts, and which of them was producing the more hideous din would have been difficult to adjudicate without the assistance of a decibel meter. Luckily the tune had just run its course, and in the intervening pause I mentioned the fact that we might as well think about setting off in the general direction of home.

She peered upon me with an accusing eye. "Have I not been sitting here for hours, waiting for you to come and collect me?" she demanded. "Watching you standing over there with Charlie McLaughlin and bellowing like a wounded bull, have I not been over here absolutely mortified by your antics?"

From past experience I realized that argument would be fruitless, so I nodded in a hang-dog fashion. However, at this point the fiddler had apparently cured himself of dehydration and commenced to scrape with renewed vigour, and Tat immediately joined him with her impression of the sorely wounded tom cat.

How and when we returned to Ballythread will forever remain a mystery to me, and even whether we were able to do our duty and stay with the departed until the morning remains a complete blank. I remember the pain-racked tones of the once-adoring mother hounding the two children from our bedroom at some time during my period of restless unconsciousness. And finally, forced from the comfort of the big bed by the agony of a distended bladder, I staggered to the bathroom to relieve myself.

Five

THE BETTER HALF was still snorting and snoring like a labouring traction engine, and so, manfully enduring the noise created by two efflorescing Alka Seltzers, I swallowed the foaming potion, dressed and crawled slowly down to the hotel kitchen. My appearance was greeted with stifled smiles from the staff, which I affected not to notice, and the Catch Docherty emerged from some oven and came over to me. "It's a little late for the breakfast, sir," she said, "but I'll see if I can fix something that will do you the world of good."

Short of euthanasia her confidence in the matter eluded me, but she disappeared into her larder and soon placed a bowl of cream-looking substance before me. "It's home-made chicken soup," she confided. "Get it down you, it will do you good."

I felt my stomach heave but I knew that her words of wisdom were probably correct.

"You were at the wake for poor Moira," Catch stated more than asked.

I nodded vigorously and nearly wept as a new wave of pain and nausea swept over me. However, the chicken soup did appear to have certain healing properties and I plodded through it, chewing half-heartedly on some slices of dry bread till at last I was replete. Having satisfied the inner man, I retired to the safe haven of my little office where a veritable mountain of invoices, statements, and various unintelligible Government bumph awaited my attention.

Being new not only to the country but to business, I had not yet evolved a system whereby anything that was not of immediate importance was heaved into the nearest trash can in the certain knowledge that it would be presented again at some future date, probably annotated in red, at which time something would have to be done about it. Even though Miss Docherty's mystery potion had settled the stomach, the dull throb above the temple was not conducive to clarity of thought and, after toying with some of the statements and writing out a few cheques to keep the traders happy, a flash of inspiration came upon me. I consulted my watch and found that the sun was well past the yard-arm; I also noticed a certain dryness in the larynx, a sure sign that medicinal fluid was required, and no great mental persuasion was needed to assure myself that a visit to the Holly Leaf was not only required but would be positively beneficial. Suiting action to inspiration I scuttled from the office, noted with pleasure that the staircase and reception area were deserted, and hied myself hence.

The major part of the village of Ballythread usually seemed to be overcome by the same affliction of the throat at this time of day, so I was considerably surprised to find the bar propped up by the lone figure of Charlie Byrne, the milkman.

He brightened up at my entrance and hospitably gestured that I should join him, waving to the barmaid at the same time.

"Where's the usual tribe?" I enquired.

"Oh!" he said. "Did you not know. Poor Moira Gull is for burying this morning."

"Ah!" I said knowingly. "I was at the wake last night."

Charlie eyed me knowingly in return. "I was wondering what ailed you," he said with a smile. "You look like a sick rat peering through a stook of straw."

Vera had just finished the delicate task of setting the thick white head of my pint and she placed it before me.

"Better give him a wee half as well," said Charlie.

I protested that I rarely imbibed spirits and in any case had consumed enough the night before to keep me going for at least a month, but I might as well have been speaking to the wall; the small glass of amber liquid was placed reverently alongside the pint.

"It will do you good," intoned the milkman.

"If that's the case, everyone round here should be bursting with health," I retorted.

"You'll be needing it," he said, "for it will be a busy day for you at the hotel later."

I nodded politely, sipped at the whiskey, then at the pint. "Why?" I asked casually.

"You have the funeral lunch," he stated. "I thought that's why you weren't at the burying."

The second gulp of whiskey was burning its way down my throat when the importance of this information suddenly sank in, causing me to choke. Charlie beat me heartily on the back to assist recovery.

"My God!" I spluttered.

A thousand mental pictures flashed through my mind of mourners arriving in long columns, all clasping their stomachs, ravenous from lack of nourishment, only to be informed that the new boss had forgotten to mention anything about a dinner, so there was none. My reputation would never survive such a terrible happening; possibly I might not either.

I leapt from the stool as though propelled by dynamite. "Phone, phone," I bleated with such pathos and earnestness that Vera practically threw me at the ancient instrument hanging on the wall.

The telephone system in Ballythread had, in all probability, been installed by the late Mr Edison. I wound frantically at the handle on the side. My efforts were rewarded by a slight humming noise and a few electrical clicks. I wound again. An eternity of time seemed to pass before the cool voice of the operator, sounding as though she were residing on some remote mountain-top in the middle of Russia, filtered down the line.

"Give me the hotel," I groaned.

Whirring noises and a succession of buzzes commenced and continued until I nearly wept with frustration. Finally a voice answered and with a sigh of relief I recognized that it was the cook.

"My God! Catch!" I wailed. "There's a funeral lunch for Mrs Gull."

"So there is," she answered in a calm and collected manner. "For fifty-eight it was at the last count."

"But I've arranged nothing," I moaned.

"Don't be fretting and worrying your head," she replied. "Didn't I have Theresa and Dymphna set up the tables after breakfast this morning, and wee Margaret from Reception is going to help as waitress when they sit down. I've roast beef or chicken and ham for them, and Ann Marie has called Gerry O'Shea from her bed to help in the bar."

"What shall I do?" I asked plaintively.

"I'd say you should take a few pints to calm yourself," she replied. "They won't be here for near an hour, and then it will take the devil himself to shift them from the bar. If you come back in about two hours you'll be able to bid them all farewell and give them the bill."

She must have replaced the receiver for the line reverted to its peculiar buzzing. I staggered back to the bar and slumped in the seat next to Charlie, who had been listening to my conversation with a half smile on his face. He had also seen to it that our glasses were replenished during my absence.

"It was your round, so I ordered for you," he explained.

I gulped gratefully and felt the ice-cold fingers of impending disaster slowly recede with the realization that everything appeared to be under control.

"Good Lord, Charlie, I nearly had a heart attack. I don't remember anyone mentioning a funeral dinner, but then I don't remember much about last night at all."

He chortled happily. "Never, never worry," he said. "They would have noticed that you weren't there to do business and would have got directly on to Catch. A good girl, that one. A funny thing around here. Every one worries themselves sick, yet at the heel of the hunt everything sorts itself out."

He launched into a long story concerning the history of one of his cows which had experienced trouble in calving, and how the hired man had been sent to get the vet but had only managed to reach the first pub. By sheer coincidence the vet had popped in there to quench his thirst, and so the message had been duly passed on.

"So you see," he concluded, "if old Jim had done as he was told and had gone straight to the vet, he wouldn't have been there, and the poor beastie would have died. As it was, I got a nice calf and the cow is one of my best milkers."

The effort of recounting this anecdote had apparently renewed his raging thirst and Vera rushed to assuage it.

We continued to chat while I recovered from my mental ordeal and, finally, when he left to continue on his milk round, I felt considerably more relaxed and composed, and returned to the hotel.

Charlie's prognosis had been correct and the main bar was packed with a variety of faces, some of whom I hazily remembered from the wake, and I was therefore able to move amongst them and commiserate with the family members closest to the deceased. After a while Tat appeared, slightly white in the face, but this could have been put down to grief unless one knew otherwise.

"There you are," she hissed menacingly. "Would you stop running around entertaining them and move them into the dining-room. The meal is going to be ruined." She looked at me accusingly, as though this event was entirely my fault, and mine alone.

"How in the name of heaven do I do that?" I asked. "I can scarcely get out a stock whip and drive them in like cattle."

"Just tell the women that the meal is ready and that they can take their glasses into the dining-room with them. Once they get on the move most of the men will follow, and Ann Marie will chase the worst ones in by and by."

To my surprise this gambit worked like magic and soon a trickle became a flood, all moving towards the meal.

I was considerably amused by one of the well-known local characters who, it appeared, always attended the hotel, clad in his best suit, when there was a funeral dinner, sublimely confident that he would be offered his fill of drink and, eventually, to partake in the meal itself. This occasion was no exception and he was in the forefront of the moving line. As he passed me he grabbed me firmly by the sleeve.

"The last three funeral lunches I've been to here," he accused *sotto voce*, "have been roast beef or chicken and ham. Can't you cook any other damn thing?"

He moved on reverently to pay his respects.

I was amazed at the efficiency of the whole operation. Girls seemed to be running in all directions, yet everyone was being served piping-hot soup and fresh bread rolls were placed on the tables like miniature mountains. I stood out of the way and watched the performance. Eventually piles of dirty and used soup bowls made their appearance in the wash-up area, and Catch moved calmly to the hot oven and arranged stackers for the main meal plates to be placed upon. Nonchalantly she slid apart the aluminium roller doors. Several of the girls moved closer, clutching their serving towels over their arms, waiting to collect the dishes and fill their respective stackers.

There was a tremendous crash, closely followed by another, and two plates of chicken and ham, together with stuffing and liberal portions of residual fat smashed onto the tiled floor.

This occurrence was greeted by loud cheers and some applause from the assembly in the dining-room but Catch, her composure destroyed, turned white with horror and cast a beseeching look towards the heavens, then literally threw her body across the front of the decanting hot oven.

"Holy Jesus!" she wept. "The bloody shelf has tipped. Quick, all of you, grab the plates."

From orderly efficiency the affair rapidly disintegrated into complete farce. The waiting waitresses lunged towards the offending oven, neglecting to notice the ever-widening pools of grease that were spreading over the floor from the first two broken plates. Slipping and sliding they clutched at Catch only to be blasted with a heat scarcely exceeded by the open oven. Finally, one plonked her backside down on the floor and like some mad puppet, began to pass out plates and separators from around the outflung arms of the cook.

I scurried into the upper part of the kitchen and, with a flash of inspiration, grabbed an armful of old newspapers from under the sink. With scant regard to hygiene I began to hurl them over the floor in the vicinity of the accident, and slowly things returned to normal. The tilted top shelf was cleared of plates and the girls started to carry them into the dining-room.

Slowly Catch straightened up. Her spotless white overall was streaked with a mixture of various foodstuffs, dominated by lengthy gravy stains, and trickles of perspiration ran down her face.

"God, but that was close," she muttered.

I peered with pity upon her bedraggled form.

"What now?" I asked.

"Vodka and white lemonade with plenty of ice, please," she said, easing herself onto the kitchen table.

I rushed to the bar and prepared a liberal shot of the colourless fluid, then, on second thoughts, I pulled a pint for myself. On entering the kitchen with the libations I found that things had returned to semi-normality; the second cook had taken over the preparation of the sweets and the girls were again rushing in and out of the dining-room as though nothing untoward had occurred. Catch grabbed the profferred glass and we both drank deeply. I peeped into the dining-room and found that all was continuing to run smoothly, so, finishing my pint, I took myself out into the open air.

I had just finished a contemplative cigarette when noise from the inside informed me that the funeral party had concluded their meal and were leaving the dining-room. Looking suitably miserable, I stood close at hand and was duly complimented on the fine meal that they had all enjoyed. I heaved a sigh of relief and gently tried to shepherd them in the general direction of the bar. This attempt was greatly appreciated by the chief mourners, but was accompanied by loud lamentations from the invited guests.

"I just couldn't. I've a cow in calf."

"I have to go and tend my ewes."

"It's the mother: she's all alone."

"If Paddy leaves, me lift has gone."

All these excuses did not seem to deter the general shuffling movement of the feet of the protesters in the direction of the bar, and soon all were seated around tables and barmaids were rushing in all directions to supply the needs of the occasion. As time passed tongues were loosened and quips and badinage by the assembled members of the company were greeted by ever more piercing laughter, especially from the female members, and after a few hours it was *de rigueur* to join in the sing-song. My Tat hovered anxiously in the background to see that the general level of merriment continued and that no person would choose the opportunity to open old scores or family disagreements of many years ago; also, I presumed, to keep a wary eye on me to see that I too was not overcome by the occasion. In this she need not have worried, for the activities of the night of the wake and the trauma of the day had left me with no desire to continue the punishment that my stomach, not to mention my head, had taken. Eventually, after what I would have described as an age, the mourners began to depart, tottering on their respective ways and leaving a litter of empty glasses and a thick fug of cigarette smoke to denote their passing.

Six

SEVERAL DAYS PASSED with all running smoothly. I have since discovered, with experience, that this is invariably the case in business. It was usually a case of the lull before the storm. So it was that I entered the kitchen one evening to find my hard-working staff sitting around the table in the top part of the area, all peering intently at the table with expressions of rapt attention on their faces.

Theresa and Dymphna, the waitresses, clung to the wash-up girl, Norette, and Peggy McShane, one of the barmaids, huddled close to Paula, the upstairs girl. Squeezed in between these two groups was Margaret, whom I had nicknamed Spot because she was so small and who did the reception and billing. Presiding over this little assembly was Muriel, the relief cook, who appeared whenever Catch had a day off. She stood peering fixedly at the table upon which she had placed a sharp pointed knife surrounded by scraps of paper, each one annotated with letters of the alphabet.

"Is anybody there?" she demanded in a ghostly voice.

"What in the name of God are you all doing?" I asked.

It had always been a mystery to me how a nation of people as religious as the Irish professed to be could quite happily believe in fairies, ghosts and secular miracles of various kinds.

"Ah!" said Muriel. "If we all concentrate, and the departed are about, they will spell out a message for some person in the company."

"Is that so?" I replied politely. "Well, I'm afraid that you'll be disappointed: there isn't a ghost in the universe that would come down here with all of you sitting under neon lights. What you need are the candlesticks from the dining-room. Light them up and turn out the big overhead lights and you might have some chance of success; in fact, I've often seen it happen if the aura is right."

Tiny Margaret jumped up and went into the dining-room, to re-appear with a candelabrum that we put on the tables in the evenings to make the place look more intimate. The candles were lit, lights turned out, and even I was surprised at the difference in atmosphere that the candle-light made in the large area of the kitchen.

With studied nonchalance I moved towards the door. "I'll leave you to it," I said, and made my exit.

Like an Olympic sprinter I dashed through the bar and out into the yard through the Gents toilets and, with the agility of a cat, swarmed up the steps of the fire escape. I arrived on the flat roof of the dining-room and crept on tip-toes over to the plastic dome set over the kitchen to allow more daylight to enter the cooking area. Cautiously I cocked an eye over the edge of the dome; I was directly over the table where the girls were gathered. The flickering candles illuminated the scene with a ghostly light and Muriel stood poised above the knife and the scraps of paper like some ancient witch beginning an incantation. Clear as a bell her voice floated up to me.

"Is anybody there?" she called. "Is there a spirit present? Speak to us."

I let out a bellow like some unfortunate bull being dragged to the slaughter, and at the same time I hammered with the palms of my hands on the plastic dome.

My efforts were rewarded about ten times more that I had

allowed for: the shrieks of pure terror from the girls must have been audible over the whole of the town. They looked petrified, incapable of movement, and clung to each other uttering noises that varied between a train whistle and the much-vaunted pitch of the banshee. Quickly I rushed from my position, down the fire escape, through the Gents, and strolled slowly up to the bar. "Give me a half of beer," I requested. The barmaid obliged and I stood resting against the counter.

Out of the corner of my eye I saw the main door of the bar open and a white and terrified face peep around it, then another.

"It couldn't have been him," announced the first face.

"No, to be sure, there he is sipping at his beer," commented the second.

The door closed and I allowed a few minutes to elapse, then strolled into the kitchen. The neon lights were glaring and the girls were huddled together as if in fearsome anticipation. Even my entry caused them to nearly jump out of their skins. I was immensely impressed by the way that they clustered closely around me as though I might be able to protect them from the demon that they were convinced their efforts had caused to rise from the pit.

"Any luck?" I asked. "Shall I have a go – let's see if I can get anything to appear. The last time I did it I managed to get one of the imps that guard the sacred goat of Hades."

A renewed round of wailing greeted my generous offer, and it was as if there were a hundred small voices all making their point at the same time. I gathered that the imp had not only appeared but that the goat had tried to break into the kitchen and all had heard his terrible hooves pounding on the roof trying to get at them and drag them back to the fires of eternal hell. Lady Paula, slightly tear-stained, maintained that they should all go and confess the awful thing that they had done to the parish priest and, if he forgave them, he might come down and exorcise the place; another suggested that they go to Ann Marie, for they were assured that she had a vast stock of holy water and that might do the trick.

I saw that my brilliant idea of a small joke had gone too far, but I realized that I could not confess to my involvement or I should either be disbelieved or, more likely, torn limb from limb. I decided that my only chance of survival would be to remove the ghostly spirit, and with due solemnity asked if they would like me to do the necessary incantations. The offer was greeted with unanimous approval and, presumably, they were under the impression that since I was a heathen anyway I might well be able to do such a thing with the ease of long practice.

"We'll have to turn out the lights," I said.

One of them reached out, and once again the only illumination was from the flickering candles. I turned on a look of what I hoped would pass for deep concentration and raised my hands as if trying to reach the upper heavens. My mind raced as I stood poised. What I needed was a really impressive incantation.

I let out a low moan, then:

"Ye imps and demons from the pit,
begone when once these lights are lit.
Your journey here has been in vain,
So never more return again."

I waited a few seconds so that the full impact of this directive could be understood by my huddled and trembling audience, then I switched on the lights.

"There," I said. "That's so powerful that unless I call them up again myself they won't be back. Still, if I were you I shouldn't try it again."

A piping chorus of female voices assured me that nothing was further from their minds, and some withering looks were directed towards Muriel, as though having been the instigator of their misfortune she was being held solely to blame.

"Now," I said. "The immense concentration and the outflow of energy needed to banish demons leaves one quite weak, so I think that I'll just wander into the bar and have a brandy. I'll leave everything in your capable hands; I'm sure that you'll have everything running smoothly for the next couple of hours while I recover."

I was overwhelmed by the tirade of grateful thanks for delivering them from the terrible clutches of the sacred goat and I was assured that I need not move a muscle ever again, that they would look after each detail and the food and service would exceed perfection. So, well pleased with my efforts, I adjourned before any awkward questions might crop up regarding my immense knowledge of the occult.

My inner delight and satisfaction at my own brilliance were slightly dampened a short while later. Tat arrived and hopped up on a bar stool beside me. "You bastard," she hissed, under her breath. "I've just been regaled with the story of the séance. I don't know how you did it, but the girls think you're some kind of gift from heaven, with complete power over the spirits. I told them the kind of spirits you have power over!"

"Did they believe you?" I asked innocently.

"No," she snarled. "So I'll just recover my psychic energy and have a vodka and lemonade."

As she sipped at her libation I could see that something was troubling her. Finally she could resist no longer.

"How did you do it?"

I looked suitably mysterious.

"It could be dangerous if I told you. We shouldn't meddle with things that we don't fully understand. Still, I reckon the spirits will keep the girls on their toes for a few days at least."

The weeks passed with no untoward incidents, and gradually an occasional appearance of the sun, which came out with all the reluctance of a virgin performing her first striptease, reassured the population that it still resided somewhere in the sky beyond the seemingly never-ending cloud banks that had become a permanent feature of life in Ballythread. Eventually the clouds thinned, the prevailing winds reversed direction, and summer was upon us.

It was now that Donegal could be appreciated by even the most blasé of holiday-makers. Flowers bloomed in the green fields and the harshness of the mountains was broken by vast patches of bright, yellow-flowering shrubs, known locally as whins. To drive slowly through the narrow roads, all edged with a variety of brightly coloured blossoms and along the coast roads with their endless miles of empty beaches, golden sands glistening in the radiant beams from above, was to obtain a contentment seldom achieved in the more populated areas of the country. Each new turn revealed a more beautiful panorama and the towering slopes of mountains like Slieve

League, Errigal and the sheer cliffs of Benbulben provided so magnificent a backdrop as to make the average person feel very small and humble.

The tourists and visitors arrived almost in a direct ratio to the increasingly fine weather. Coaches trundled into the town and decanted their human cargoes to gaze upon and photograph the fishing boats tied up at the pier, and the Pier Gate grew more busy as the volume increased. I was amazed at the variety of nationalities that arrived in this remote fishing village. Strange notes – lira, francs, dollars, guilders and even pesos – began to appear in the bar till, and each morning a ritual phone call to the local bank was necessary to elicit the correct exchange to be given for the various currencies. I found, as no doubt had many before me, that with the coming of fine weather the unfortunate hotelier, and the staff, were not able to enjoy it. As the volume of visitors grew, dark murmurings among the staff urged an increase in their numbers. I held out against recruiting more girls for as long as possible, but when the schools broke up for the summer holidays I was swamped by the arrival of countless young ladies in Reception, all professing themselves to be skilled at hotel work and all willing to do absolutely anything so long as they could earn a few pounds during the holidays. Finally I broke down and hired two of the young hopefuls who, since they were both named Theresa, we christened "T.1" and "T.2". They were employed under the all-purpose title of general workers and threw themselves into their various allotted tasks with the enthusiasm of the very young.

It was about this time that the smooth and even tenor of the business was enlivened by the arrival of a couple from the North of Ireland, an immaculately dressed and charming gentleman and his lady, an attractive though slightly plump blonde. It looked as though they might be newly married for she clung to him with pathetic reliance and, at his every utterance, gazed up into his face with an adoring look. I mentioned my assumption that they were newly-weds to Ann Marie but, though offering no counter-argument, she looked at me with a very knowing eye.

"Them's no more married that I am," she pronounced. "Them two come here every year – always the same – look like they are the perfect loving couple, but he spends most of his time beating her."

I was astonished and, in fact, thought that she might have been using what is commonly known as artistic licence in telling her story of the couple.

Ann Marie went off to the wilds that evening to enjoy her day off with her sister who lived in a small croft perched precariously on the side of a nearby mountain, and it was left to me to close up the hotel at the time appointed by law. This I duly did, and in the course of ejecting the assembled customers who considered closing time to be an intolerable infringement on their personal liberty, I noticed that the two love-birds were still entwined in a small alcove in the bar. Being residents, I left them until the last of the outside customers had been urged upon their way, all protesting vigorously that if they had been served with just "one more wee half" they would have left anyway. I turned out the bar lights and moved over to the couple and suggested that they might like to retire to the Residents' Lounge and, should they desire it, I would be only too pleased to supply them with a tray of whatever drinks they would like to consume. There was a short consultation, then the man announced that they would retire to bed and would not trouble me any more. With the help of the duty barmaid I cleaned the bar so that it would be ready for the morning, checked the till, secured all the doors and, upon completion, dismissed the barmaid, who scampered out as if the devil were on her heels, presumably to frequent one of the numerous bars that relied upon after-hours custom to exist.

It is a tried and true axiom that every person who stays in a hotel is well versed in the expertise necessary to turn on an electric light but is incompetent to the point of complete ignorance in the skill required to turn one off. Consequently, having closed the bar, it had become my practice to patrol the premises turning out the numerous corridor lights, toilet lights, and the television and lights in the Residents' Lounge, and generally tucking up the place for sleep, and this evening was no exception. I switched off all the third-floor lights, meandered down the stairs to the second floor, and repeated the process. I was passing room four when I heard a peculiar noise. A strange whimpering sound, like that of a chastened puppy, emanated from behind the closed door. Though I would have reprimanded an eavesdropper, I was forced to stop and listen.

"Do you deserve more?" a harsh male voice growled.

"Yes, yes," a tearful-sounding female voice replied. "I have been a very bad girl, haven't I?"

"You have," he answered. "Turn over."

By this time my ears were flapping like the proverbial rhubarb leaves, and I moved silently nearer to the door.

"Push it up," ordered the man.

There was a rustle of movement, then the creak of bed springs.

His command had apparently been obeyed, for the next sound was like the explosion of a small firecracker. With the precision of a metronome the crack echoed again and again, and it did not require the deductive ability of a top Scotland Yard detective to realize that the sounds were similar to those that would be occasioned by the hard contact of a hand on a bare bottom.

I paused, my mind in a turmoil. Should I burst into the room and stop this ill treatment, or should I collect the master keys and make a more dignified entrance and stop the action? As the cracks continued, I hesitated. No word of complaint came from the recipient when she could have shouted for aid. Probably because of the state of my mind the cracks appeared to continue for hours, but then murmured voices announced that the activity was completed and the bed springs creaked with even greater vigour.

I moved away and down the stairs, making a mental note that I should have to do something in the morning to evict the twosome, and probably reap the benefit of the gratefulness of the poor unfortunate woman. I slept fitfully, my mind in a turmoil over the affair for, though by no means a prude and, I would have contended, quite knowledgeable of between-the-sheets activities, I had read widely but never graduated to the more erotic realms of sado-masochism. Thus it was with a modicum of surprise that I saw the couple coming down the stairs in the morning for their breakfast, once more entwined and, if anything, the blonde gazing even more adoringly at her escort. I followed them into the dining-room and noted with disbelief that she plonked her curvaceous behind down on the hard chair and scrutinized the menu with single-minded enjoyment. Obviously her squire had done nothing to achieve any lasting effect upon her nether regions.

This presented me with a quandary. After all, they had offended no one, seemed to be perfectly happy and, indeed, might object strongly if they were notified that their nocturnal activities had, in effect, been spied upon. I decided that in the circumstances discretion was the better part of valour, and resolved to seek the wisdom and vast experience of Ann Marie on the subject when she returned from her day off. When she arrived that evening I engaged the faithful retainer in conversation, general at first, then brought up the subject of the strange couple.

Ann Marie smiled knowingly. "I just lets them get on with it," she announced. "When they first come here, quite a few years ago, I heard their goings on when I was locking up and I went to the pantry and fetched the master keys. I just opened the door and walked in. What did I see? There was the buck stretched out on the bed twirling the keys to the room on his finger, not a care in the world on him."

She paused for effect.

"Not a sign of the woman at all at all. Quite took me aback it did. I was just about to apologize and say that I'd made a mistake when I heard this noise from the wardrobe, so I opens the door and out pops this woman, naked as a jaybird, and off she scoots through the open door and away down the corridor. All I could see was a big red behind before she turns the corner and locks herself in the toilet. The buck doesn't turn a hair, and so I just moved off. Would you believe that she, herself, comes to me in the morning and announces that they were just playing a game and she hopes that they didn't disturb anyone. After that, whenever they come I just let them play away."

"Indeed," she sighed and looked towards heaven, "you get some strange ones come to stay in a hotel; now I just lets things take their appointed course."

With a feeling of some relief I decided that she was correct and so did nothing and, in fact, after a few days grew quite used to the sounds of flagellation that came from their room every night when I roamed the corridors turning out the lights.

Seven

AS MY TENURE as a proprietor lengthened I heeded that wisdom of Ann Marie. Many and varied indeed were the clientele that passed through the doors. Some were obviously tourists, here for a holiday away from the cares of city life, but some, usually quite withdrawn and seemingly furtive, appeared and disappeared after a short stay, with no apparent reason for their travels and no business transacted. Likewise, as the season progressed and the number of visitors to the hotel increased, I began to have doubts as to the wisdom of our move to the Emerald Isle.

The Pier Gate could certainly not be accused of lacking atmosphere and, as for antiquity, it was in all probability the oldest structure in the village. But the countless additions to the original building had never taken account of minor considerations like the size of piping, the strain on the wiring or the supply of hot water to the extra bedrooms. Consequently, we were continually attacked by visitors who had been unable to get a bath when they wanted one and who, in some cases, in the upper rooms, could get no water at all. Fuses were purchased by the dozen but, since no one apparently knew which fuse serviced what part of the building, were replaced by a method of trial and error. Each fuse was moved one to the right in sequence until something went out, and then the offending fuse was replaced by a new one.

This system apparently worked well, except that through the course of time the loading of the fuses had been increased to an extent where it was more likely that the wire would blow rather than the fuse. The fuse that usually blew belonged to my Tat, for it was she, in her capacity of manageress, who was sent to deal with the more acrimonious visitors who took umbrage over one or the other of these occurrences. My beloved would then tour the whole place, peering and peeping, until she finally located the hiding place that I had chosen for the day. I was then treated to a lecture on the inadequacies of the various systems, as though all construction through the countless years had been achieved under my personal supervision and thus all such failures could be directly attributed to my negligence and lack of forethought. This harangue would send me scuttling off to locate a plumber or an equally harrassed electrician. By means known only to themselves they would usually manage to rectify the fault, at least for a few days, until some other disaster would send me flying for their assistance once again.

The electrician was a young man new to the town, having trained across the water and then returned with his wife. As he traced the coils of ancient wire that ran in profusion all over the walls and under the floorboards, his wonderment would increase.

"According to all the electrical text books," he once confided to me, "this rig shouldn't work at all. One of these days there will be a gigantic flash and the whole damn building will fall in a heap!"

He paused for breath.

"Do you know, I traced that fuse that is always blowing – the one in the kitchen. It supports twenty-nine lights, runs the water boiler, and some clown has put in a multi-point adaptor to one of the six plugs in the wall that it also feeds and is running two deep-freezes off it."

"Can you keep it going until the rush is over?" I pleaded.

He uttered a long sigh. "I suppose so, but I wouldn't dare do it in England. It's been running so long now it will probably run for ever; but don't ask me how."

We left it at that and I grew used to putting my hand deep into my pocket to pay him and the other men of genius who managed to keep us operational.

Only once did I flatly refuse to settle one of the most outrageous accounts presented for such services rendered, and this was from an individual who had been called upon after we had suffered a particularly long spell without hot water in the building. The local genius of the plumbing world had laboured long and hard to solve this problem, hammering and banging far into the night, to the ever greater aggravation of the guests, but, for all the vigour of his attacks, the monster of an oil-fired boiler continued to roar happily away, consuming gallon upon gallon of expensive fuel oil without apparently achieving anything for its efforts. In the end he admitted defeat and suggested that my only hope would be to contact a man of immense learning in the lore of boilers, who resided some distance away in the town of Ballykenny.

After an hour of frustration attempting to establish contact via the crumbling telephone system, a faint voice in the earpiece notified me that my efforts had been successful and that I was indeed speaking to McShane, plumber and window cleaner. I howled out our troubles with the system and explained that no matter what we did no hot water would appear in the top cylinder, and would he kindly fix it. We shrieked and bellowed down the respective mouthpieces for some time, and finally he agreed that he would undertake the journey to Ballythread and solve the problem. From the intonation in his voice I got the general message that his presence in person would involve a considerable investment but, with Tat attacking me at every turn and visitors grumbling incessantly, it was no time to be parsimonious.

With my throat sore from my efforts in communications it was with a feeling of achievement that I left the phone back on the hook and strode through the premises assuring all and sundry that the problem was in hand and, if they would have the patience to wait the coming of this new and greatly respected brain, all our troubles would be over and water would flow from the taps in a never-ending and steaming flood, as though the place were constructed over a hot spring. This assurance had the effect of placating the guests and in some degree my beloved Tat, who, though appreciative of my efforts, still had her doubts.

The following morning I patrolled the reception area like a palace sentry on guard, swathed in a glow of self-righteousness, awaiting the promised arrival of the swami of plumbing and central heating. As the morning progressed I began to feel that my efforts might have been in vain, for there was no sign of the coming of the great one.

Lunchtime, and I moodily sipped a beer in the bar, wondering what particular miracle I could perform should this paragon not put in an appearance but coming up with a complete blank. At best I should be subjected to a vicious tongue-lashing by Tat, but at worst the visitors might pack their bags and leave *en bloc* – a disaster not seriously to be contemplated.

I was peering sorrowfully at the dregs of my pint when a small face appeared in my line of vision. It was Norette Lovett, the wash-up girl. I sighed, waiting for the announcement that she had flooded the kitchen, burnt out the dishwasher, or some other tragedy, these occasions being the only times that I had ever had speech with her outside of the days when, wet and covered with soap-suds, she appeared to collect her wages.

"There's a man looking for you," she said softly, as though she was portending the end of the world.

"Who?" I asked.

"I don't know him," she replied. "But he says that his name is Mickey McShane, says that you know about it."

A great weight lifted from my mind and I sprang from the stool with the agility of a gazelle that had spotted a lion.

At equal speed my heart fell when I reached the lobby. Literally clinging to the reception desk was a man of such ancient years that it was a wonder that he had not been forced to take oxygen in order to climb the steps at the entrance of the hotel. He gripped the desk as though the effort had really been too much for him and any further activity would be completely out of the question. I approached with some trepidation, and as I neared him my nostrils informed me that he probably had good reason to appear distraught and weary. An unbiased opinion could well conclude that the poor fellow had been caught in the explosion of a distillery. The slight draught from the front door caused the redolent fumes he breathed to travel towards me in an alcoholic cloud that would have crossed the eyes of any animal not provided with protective goggles. Cautiously I circled round and approached from up-wind. This appeared to cause him great surprise, for he remained staring fixedly at the door through which I had made my appearance. Taking a deep breath I moved nearer. However, my trouble had been in vain. His efforts had obviously exhausted him to a degree that he could no longer tolerate, and his eyes were firmly closed as he rested in the vertical position.

This placed me with a considerable conundrum. If I touched him he might fall, or have a heart attack. He could become violently sick or, worse, think he was in the toilet and relieve himself all over the reception carpet. Yet, if I didn't, then we should continue to have no hot water and, for all I knew, he might remain in a comatose condition for the remainder of the summer. My dilemma was resolved when Ann Marie passed through the area. I grimaced and raised my hands in a gesture of supplication, and she waddled over.

"What's that?" she enquired, peering upon the recumbent one with a jaundiced eye.

I explained his purpose, his name, and what I had hoped from him, and she giggled heartily.

"Let's get him on the job then," she chortled and before I could remonstrate she drew back her foot and delivered a lusty kick to the sleeping man's left ankle.

The ancient one leapt from the desk as though having received an electric shock and treated us to an exhibition of right-footed dancing that would have done credit to an Oul' Naile dancer with colic.

"Ho!" said Ann Marie. "Let's have none of your old

malarky, Mickey McShane. Get in there and fix the boiler or I'll kick the other ankle."

"Jesus, Mary and Joseph!" howled the hopping ancient. "Are you not dead yet, you old witch? If I'd have known I'd not have come."

"Fat lot of good you've done so far," she retorted. "Now, get on with you."

"Show me where it is," he moaned with an appealing look at me. I started to move and he limped along in my wake, glad to excuse himself from the proximity of Ann Marie's foot.

I pointed him at the offending boiler but by this time my faith in his ability had completely evaporated and I had concluded that I might as well have pointed him at the gas oven for all the good that he was going to do.

"Have you a screwdriver, sir?" he groaned in a servile voice.

I produced one and he gestured to a small plate set in the side of the tank. "Would you unscrew that and read what it says to me?" he requested. "You see, I've mislaid me glasses somewhere and I'll need to study the problem."

Solemnly I removed the plate from the thermostat and read out the voltages, watts, serial number, etc. annotated thereon, while the ancient absorbed these gems of wisdom as if seeking inspiration from them. He felt the top of the cylinder, nearly fell as he bent down and attempted to feel the bottom, and then completed his repertoire by venting a large belch which should, by all rights, have resulted in an explosion, before announcing that he would depart and dwell upon the problem. In order that there would not be a law suit for negligence should he fall while leaving the premises, I escorted him to the door and watched with awe as he progressed like an arrow from a bow and finally disappeared from my sight through the portals of the Fisherman's Bar across the street. I realized that because of his complete failure I was likely to be subjected to a torrent of abuse from the guests, and the frightful reaction of my wife was too terrible to dwell on.

Drooping and abject, I returned to the boiler room and attempted to replace the plate that I had removed for his edification. Such was my ability at do-it-yourself that I had great difficulty in even replacing the screws, and finally managed to get three back in place; the hole wherein the fourth should have been placed must have moved during my absence, and I finally hurled the screw away in disgust. As a parting gesture I delivered a mighty kick in the general direction of the thermostat and, to my horror, the boiler fired again with a mighty thud. Ashes blew in clouds from behind the steel door and a great rushing and gurgling noise rocked and vibrated the cylinder. Enough is enough! Terrified at what I had achieved I firmly closed the door to the room, slunk from the hotel and headed for the Holly Leaf to drown my sorrows.

Here, merriment was in progress, and my idea of a quiet drink while I meditated upon my problem was soon dispelled. Time passed quickly, and with a stab of guilt I realized that evening grills were now in progress and that I should be back in my own place. Like some thief in the night I slid into Reception, through the bar, nodding amiably to acknowledge the customers, and then into the kitchen. Tat greeted me with what, for her, was practically rapture.

"You managed it!" she shouted. "I told you from the start if only you got someone that knew what he was doing there would be no problem."

How I managed to keep my face straight was little short of a miracle, firstly because I hadn't the faintest idea of what she was raving about and, secondly, such praise from that particular source was unusual to say the least. At first I suspected that she might be sarcastically pulling my leg, but then light dawned as I watched the hot, steaming water flowing from the taps in the kitchen. I modestly accepted the plaudits, then made a rapid exit before I was asked more difficult questions on the subject.

It was with a feeling of complete disbelief that I opened an official brown envelope tucked in the pile of morning mail some days later. It was headed, *McShane, Plumber and Window Cleaner*, and in a most official fashion listed his services and the charge for same.

To locating and diagnosing trouble in upper cylinder head of central heating boiler:	£12.00
To time, labour and travelling expenses:	£28.00
Total:	£40.00

I could not show this document to Tat or she would have to be told the truth and would no doubt not believe it, now being firmly of the opinion that the wisdom of the ancient was worth every penny of his charge; never would I be able to convince her that a hefty kick had actually solved the problem. I had confided the actual state of affairs to Ann Marie, who had been in the bar during the plumber's short sojourn in the boiler-room, so I went now to seek her advice.

She cluck-clucked like a laying hen. "Mickey," she laughed. "He couldn't locate or diagnose a bunion on his own foot."

"What shall I do about it?" I asked plaintively.

Deliberately she tore the bill into small pieces.

"He's only trying it on," she said. "If he comes back again to try to collect, you send him in to me and I'll scalp the wee devil." She wandered away smiling to herself, and there, to this day, the matter rests. Needless to say, Mickey McShane never darkened the doorstep again.

Eight

THE COSMOPOLITAN NATURE and sensual proclivities of the guests never ceased to amaze me, but some weeks passed before anything out of the ordinary happened. It was Lady Paula, the housekeeper and bedroom girl, who usually detected occurrences of an unusual nature.

"We've a strange one," she announced one morning.

"How strange?" I enquired, feeling my heart sink.

"In number eight," she replied. "Says she's from Drumshannon. All on her own, she is; gets up about noon and heads straight for the bar. You must have seen her – small, dark-haired, and with the same clothes ever since she's been here."

"What about her?" I asked. I had seen a woman who fitted the description hanging around the bar on several occasions, usually having a drink with one or other of the fishermen who frequented the premises but, beyond that, I'd noticed nothing peculiar about her.

Paula lowered her voice and looked conspiratorially around to see if we were being overheard.

"Well, when I do her room out the bed always looks as if a storm had hit it; there's always a pile of empty glasses to take away and," she paused dramatically, "there's always a pile of cigarette stubs in the ashtray, and only about half of them have lipstick on them, and that's the tipped ones. I think she is taking men into her room."

An immediate vision of standing in the dock being charged with running a disorderly house flashed into my mind.

"God! We'll have to give her the bums' rush, Lady Paula."

"Ah!" said the upstairs girl. "That's the crack: this morning she asked one of the barmaids to come up to the room with her and she gives her the blouse and slacks that she's been wearing all the time and asks her to take them to the dry cleaners, and, not knowing that she had nothing else to wear, she did. Your one is up there now sitting on the bed with nothing on but her skin, for she's washed out her underwear in the sink and has it drying over the radiator."

To state that I gaped at her would be the understatement of the year. What to do? Lady Paula had held me in great regard since my number five iron had solved one of her problems, and I did not want to destroy her faith in my ability to solve any other problem that she was faced with. But women with no clothes on could not be summarily ejected onto the highway. I decided that delaying tactics would be in order.

"Was it Peggy or Gerry that took her gear?" I asked.

It transpired that it was Gerry, and since she was still on duty in the bar I went there to enquire further about "the strange one".

"Oh, yes!" said Gerry happily. "I took them down for her; she's been spending a lot in the bar and so I thought that I'd better oblige her."

Rapidly I explained the problem to her. She broke into a wide smile, then roared with laughter.

"You'll be all right there," she giggled. "I thought she was a fast one – you've got it made."

With some asperity I put it to her that I had no intention of touching her with a barge pole and asked how soon the clothes would be ready for collection from the dry cleaners.

"Well," said the barmaid, "seeing that it's a Saturday, they won't be open tomorrow so she'll probably have them ready on Monday sometime."

This news just about made my day and I tottered away to ponder on the matter. It was obvious that I would be unable to winkle her out with a five iron, and likewise a lusty kick would have little effect except to occasion a law suit for assault.

"Women!" I muttered.

This soft hiss was picked up by the delicate hearing mechanism of Tat, who happened to be passing at the same time.

"What have I done now?" she asked.

I poured out the latest woe that had befallen us.

"So," I concluded, "it looks as if I'll have to go up there and have a few hard words with the lady. She can't just lie there in the nude till the cleaners decide to open up again."

"Oh no you don't!" snapped the better half. She obviously had no more faith in the decency of my sexual proclivities than had Gerry, the barmaid. "I'll get some of my old clothes and she can dress in them. You get off to the barracks and see if the Gardaí know anything about her."

This struck me as clear, logical thinking, so I collected her signing-in chit from the reception desk and trotted up the street to visit the majesty of the law.

The Sergeant seemed to find my predicament a source of great merriment, and his great belly wobbled with mirth. But prodded into action he put through a call to the barracks in Drumshannon. He must have had some influence over the workings of the crumbling telephone system for, to my surprise, he managed to get through almost at once. He recounted the occurrence in an official voice, then pressed the receiver to his ear in fascination. All I could hear were his replies.

"Does she?"

"Indeed?"

"Does the poor creature not mind?"

Finally he scratched his skull and replaced the phone.

"She does it regular," he announced. "They just wait till some Garda station eventually phones and then the husband goes to get her. They say he has a fine business up there, and he says to hold on to her and see that she gets all the drink that she wants. The sooner she's had her fill, the sooner she'll pass out, and then he'll come and get her and take her home. Then she'll be as good as gold for another few months until she breaks out again. The Sergeant says not to worry about the bill, the man will settle all her expenses when he arrives."

I thanked him for his trouble and tore back to the hotel to communicate the good news to my beloved. She seemed to accept the situation with far more equanimity than I did myself, only pointing out in no uncertain terms that it was no doubt the disgusting and horrible brutality of the woman's husband that had reduced her to this wretched pass. As we were standing in Reception the offending lady tripped lightly down the stairs, smiled sweetly at Tat, thanked her for the loan of the clothes, and immediately adjourned to the bar.

That evening the big Sergeant arrived in the bar. He rested his ample frame upon a small stool and with no preamble ordered a pint of stout for himself and one for me, then settled back comfortably in a seat from which he could view the proceedings. "Which one is she?" he asked quietly.

I pointed the lady out. Though having propped up the bar for some six hours she showed no signs of over-indulgence. Chattering gaily to a couple of fishermen who supplied her with a continual flow of drink, she was acting the part of the belle of the ball.

My Tat had arrayed herself in evening finery and came over to join us.

"Ah!" breathed the guardian of the law. "The crack should be good: that one can't keep pouring it down like that forever."

We conversed on a variety of subjects and refreshed ourselves at frequent intervals: however, our efforts were puny compared to that of the lady. She poured vodka down herself as if she were tasting the wine of Cana. Closing time came near.

"Whee!" gusted the Sergeant. "If the bitch doesn't do something soon she'll be carrying me out instead of the other way around."

His prognostication must have telepathically communicated itself to the lady for, without turning a hair, she rose from the stool and headed for the door. To look at her one could have made an even bet that alcohol had never passed her lips. But then, just as she paused to bestow a sweet smile at Tat, she pitched forward and fell flat on her face at our feet.

The Sergeant smiled, his worst fears not having come to pass, and upon my request scooped up the recumbent figure like some fluffy doll. Tat scurried on ahead opening doors and turning on lights, and soon he deposited her back in number eight, where she lay like a sack of flour in the middle of the bed. Tat removed her shoes, and there we left her to lie.

Her spouse arrived in the morning; apparently the Garda network had passed on the information that she had had a sufficiency. He turned out to be one of the nicest fellows that I had met in a long while. He apologized to all and sundry, and would undoubtedly have apologized to the cat if we could have produced one of the wild moggies that infested the back yard. Without a qualm he paid her room account and, without turning a hair, settled the massive bar account that she had managed to run up. All this having been done he went to her room and very soon, once again looking like a sweet and innocent little girl, she came tripping down the stairs behind him, smiled sweetly at us all and passed into the street where he tenderly tucked her into a large car that stood waiting.

They passed from our view and I gave a sigh of relief, but I still await with anxiety the return of the lady.

Nine

BY THIS TIME the staff had overcome most of the apprehensions that my arrival had caused and I was able to have a bit of fun with them, and so it was on the day in question.

I had decided to cleanse the body beautiful and, equipped with bath towel, aromatic soap and other aids to personal cleanliness, adjourned to the bathroom on the first floor. I stripped off the dirty clothes that I was wearing while the water flowed into the bath tub, and was just about to immerse the said body when I discovered that I had neglected to include shampoo in my hoard of goodies. I always made a habit, much to the vocal disapproval of Tat, of washing my hair when in the bath. A dilemma faced me: whether to continue with the ablutions, neglecting the hair, and thus to incur the wrath of my beloved who contended that I bathed all too infrequently, or to depart to the chemist's shop next door elegantly clad in a bath towel. I was mulling over the problem when I heard the patter of tiny feet coming across the landing, and a short burst of song from the lips of a happy girl.

I recognized the voice as that belonging to the cook, Catch Docherty, making her way from the staff quarters in the rear of the building to the kitchen to oversee and prepare the choice viands that we were to offer to the passing throng for their lunch, should they be so disposed to feast outside the confines of their various homes. I swiftly pulled the door of the bathroom ajar and peeped through. Surely enough, my ears had been correct, and I saw the lissome figure of the cook just about to descend the stairs.

"Psssst!" I whispered in a conspiratorial fashion.

She stopped and gazed around, seeking the source of the strange sound.

"Here, Catch," I whispered.

She looked at the eye that I was exposing around the semi-opened door and, evidently recognizing the voice of the lord and master, came back.

"What's the matter?" she enquired.

I explained my problem and requested that she progress forthwith to the chemist and purchase the necessary shampoo, and with alacrity she trotted off to do my bidding. It was while I was awaiting her return that the devil made his appearance and tempted me. Patiently I awaited her coming and, poking an eye and a hand around the bathroom door I accepted the small plastic sachet she handed to me.

"Oh! Ah!" I muttered. "Thank you very much." I poked my head further round the door, looking as forlorn and sorrowful as I could as I inspected the small, inoffensive plastic container.

"What's the matter?" she asked, for having returned with the desired article she felt that she had performed her duties to the utmost.

"Nothing," I said, peering even more sorrowfully at the package. "Thank you again."

"Did you want the one that gets rid of dandruff?"

"No," I groaned. "But you only brought the one for scalp – I wanted the one for pubic as well."

"I'll go back and get it," she replied spontaneously.

She departed down the stairs, and with a swift movement I

locked the bathroom door and perched myself on the warm edge of the bath to await developments.

My wait was short, for scarcely had she time to reach the reception area when I heard a shriek and her feet came racing up the stairs again. She hammered on the bathroom door which, with great presence of mind, I kept firmly closed.

"I'll get you for this!" she howled. "Would I ever have been able to hold up my head in this town again if I had got to the shop?"

I hooted with glee and swished the water around in the tub, but evidently her source of invective had run out for I heard her trotting down the stairs again. I leisurely completed my ablutions and after a while emerged polished and gleaming, so that even Tat was moved to remark that I looked practically human, a rare compliment indeed from her.

Since our two little angels were confined to their weekly boarding school my beloved suggested that we might partake of a really nice evening meal in the dining-room. Usually we ate in our own private lounge where, frankly, I felt far more at ease but, having just emerged from the aromatic waters, she apparently felt that I could be shown off to the assembled population eating out, without her being in her usual state of mortification at my appearance. My earlier attempt at jocularity had quite slipped my mind and, accepting the easy way out, I agreed that she was right and that we did deserve to dine out in some state.

The dining-room was comparatively full when we entered, and Tat nodded and smiled at the various dignatories and friends who were busily feeding their respective faces, while I wandered along behind her with a permanent leer fixed upon my face that I fondly imagined showed the relevant bonhomie that was expected of a proprietor. Tat chose a table where she could view the assemblage and, presumably, where she herself might be inspected by them.

As soon as we were seated, Dymphna the waitress appeared as though propelled by rockets in an attempt to demonstrate her superb efficiency in the gentle art of pushing the soup. Though having made up the à la carte menu myself, with the help of the two cooks, I gave due thought to my choice, as did herself, and it occured to me that I had seen some really beautiful jumbo prawns being landed by one of the boats, and so the scampi should be most mouthwatering. Consequently, as Dymphna once again skidded to a halt at our table, I ordered some. Beloved decided to treat herself to a fillet steak and a side salad, and we both were happy.

A small portion of Irish smoked salmon to wet the appetite, with crisp home-made brown bread, and then the scampi arrived. Piles of neat brown and battered pieces, beautifully garnished with lettuce and tomatoes, a veritable feast of chips and, since I was, to all intents and purposes, out for the night, some sweet buttered asparagus tips to top the lot. I tucked into this offering with a will. Each and every scrumptuous morsel of the scampi was savoured, and the odd chip chewed to clear the palate. So delicious was the total meal that I lashed out and we ordered a carafe of the "pick of the vine for one and nine," as the house wine was known. Finally, completely replete, I rested from my labours, all the delicate crustaceans removed from my plate; in fact, precious little of any sort of food remained, and I stretched my legs out under the table with a sigh of contentment.

Dymphna appeared and commenced to remove the crockery and platters, asking anxiously if we had enjoyed our repast, and appearing happy at being given an affirmative reply. Then, from the kitchen, emerged Catch. With fluid grace she approached the table, her white smock gleaming with cleanliness. "Did you all enjoy what you ordered?" she asked.

Ice-cold fingers of fear crept around my heart: she looked too pleased by far. My efforts of earlier entertainment flooded into my mind.

"You didn't?" I asked, half fearfully. All the well known drugs flashed through my brain. Was it arsenic, rat poison, or some fiendish concoction handed down from mother to daughter in bygone years of folk legend, that she had carefully infused into my meal? Would I become sterile or half-witted; would I wither, or become covered in warts as a result of my harmless attempt at humour?

She, at any rate, appeared pleased with her efforts. "Did you enjoy your scampi?" she leered.

My worst fears were confirmed. She had done something terrible to my meal.

Tat looked astonished as I gazed pleadingly at the far too innocent-looking girl.

"Not what I should have done," she said at last. "But at least we know now who can't tell prawns from a common old monkfish around here," and with a sniff of triumph she strode off to her domain in the kitchen.

Her visitation had whet the appetite of Tat to ascertain the reason for her strange behaviour and, seeing that she would undoubtedly be informed of it from many sources, I deemed it advisable to recount the complete episode to her myself before she heard a distorted version elsewhere.

To my surprise she laughed heartily at the story, and so, except for the cook's undoubted victory, the evening passed with great conviviality.

Ten

IT IS A well known axiom in the hotel business that nobody ever does anything, especially if it is wrong. Something lost – no one has ever seen it. Anything broken – nobody touched it. The stock excuse: I wasn't on at that time. I was sometimes moved to wonder if anyone was on at any time. However, these things were internal traumas and had to be dealt with by the management. Outside his control were the guests. These came in a continual human tide, consisting of various colours, creeds and nationalities, but all had one thing in common: their respective abodes in their various countries of origin were devoid of towels in all cases, sheets in many cases, and all required a profusion of glasses, knives and forks, condiment sets and crockery. Anything not actually screwed down would eventually disappear, and the more expensive the article, the faster it would go. These basic rules hold good for all visitors except those from the United States. These worthy people were apparently well stocked with all of the above-named essentials, but were avid collectors of ashtrays and water jugs or any other items whereon a maker's name had been embellished for advertizing reasons. Whiskey companies supplied a profusion of water jugs; cigarette companies stacked the premises with ashtrays extolling the virtues of their various poisonous products, but not even the largest of these companies could keep up with the collecting capabilities of our American friends. With monotonous regularity replacements were set out for various missing articles, and on each occasion a mental note to keep an eye on it this time was duly made. But with the inevitability of day and night the piece vanished.

For some time I had been apprehensive as to the fate of a particularly nice looking and graceful pewter tea pot that decorated the mantelpiece in the reception area. It, amongst all other items of decor, seemed to bear a charmed life. All sorts of persons handled it, commented upon its value, argued as to its age, and then replaced it. After a really trying week, when I was convinced that the whole place was going to disappear out of the door unless something was done, I resolved to secure the tea pot before that too grew legs and walked off into the great unknown beyond the portals. The local hardware shop supplied me with a new and special adhesive. The virtues of this new wonder material were propounded earnestly to me by the proprietor, who promptly charged me an exorbitant sum for the stuff. Well pleased with my efforts, I returned to the hotel and, obeying the directions on the twin tubes to the letter, I bonded the pot to the red brick tile that lay in the direct centre of the mantelpiece. I hung around the reception area like a bad smell during the time that the stuff was stated to require to assume the hardness of steel. At last came the moment I'd been waiting for, and with Tat and two of the staff watching with baited breath I tried to shift it. The hardware proprietor had been correct, and the makers had surpassed themselves and produced a product that they could be proud of. The pot could have acted as a bollard for the berthing of a fairly large ship. I heaved and tugged, but it remained firmly in its appointed position.

"There," I announced. "That's one thing that the buggers won't be able to swipe."

Overcome with my own brilliance I adjourned to the Holly Leaf and ordered a pint of the black wine of the country to ward off any bug or virus that might be thinking of infecting me.

The arrival of Charlie Byrne with the milk and a few more of the local regulars, together with the chat of Paddy, the genial barman and owner and, more to the point, dispenser of refreshment, soon had our tongues wagging freely. I related my annoyance at the continual and always unsolved disappearance of things from the hotel and was rewarded by a certain degree of sympathy from the assembled company.

"How could people do things like that?"

"You should catch them and kick them."

"Give the poor fellow another jar, Paddy."

Finally I confided in them my activities relative to the precious pot and, with a certain degree of triumph, made the point that as from now anyone that had designs of a nefarious nature upon that particular item was doomed to disappointment. However, this statement did not meet with the enthusiasm and approval that I expected.

Charlie looked mournfully at me over the top of his wee half. "You shouldn't have done that," he told me.

"Why in God's name not?" I replied with some annoyance. "It would have gone sooner or later if I hadn't."

"It'll go sooner now," he advised sorrowfully. "You wait and see. They'll notice that you've sealed it down and they'll look at it as a challenge and will think that you don't trust them. You mark my words."

Conversation became general until, with a sigh, I realized that the time had come to return to the mundane life of Ballythread, and the hotel in particular, and that I must leave this haven of good fellowship. I did not forget the dire prognosis of Charlie and every time I passed through the reception area I peeped surreptitiously in the direction of the pot, each time heaving a sigh of relief as it continued to reside in its fixed and appointed place. This happy state of affairs continued until the arrival of the "luggers".

These were large factory ships which came from numerous countries, some from the free world and some from the forbidden countries behind the Iron Curtain. Many and varied were the languages and currencies that were heard and obtained in the hotel. The girls were nearly driven demented trying to oblige some swarthy looking individual, usually with no English, who, with implicit faith in the capitalist system and hardware, was trying to make contact with his beloved in Bulgaria or some other exotic sounding country through the painfully inadequate telephone system that was supposed to link the village of Ballythread with the capitals of world commerce and trade, but in most cases having its capabilities strained to the limit to reach the next small town. One was eventually driven to conclude, judging from the howls and screams that were directed at the instrument, that if the beloved Bulgar happened to be standing in the street in Sofia she would have heard her swain without the aid of telephonic communication at all.

All these seamen had been at sea for some time in order to reach our small community and so, naturally, their thirst was phenomenal, and the girls in the bar worked like dogs to ensure that they received an adequate supply of beverage during the short time that they were in the town. At the same time they also tried, in the nicest manner possible, to protect themselves from supplying the other necessity that seamen required after a prolonged stint on the billowing waves of the ocean. I counted myself blessed in that my young ladies seemed to have been imbued with this capability from birth and were able to handle the hardiest and most persistent swains with humour and decency and send them on their ways happily, without knowing quite how they happened to still require what they had originally set out to obtain. It was noticeable, however, that quite a few new female faces were to be seen in the town during this period, and it was reasonable to conclude that some of the gentlemen in question were able to satisfy their requirements, though probably returning to their vessels a good deal poorer than they had originally intended.

All this unusual activity, though delighting my bank manager, caused me much extra strain, rushing hither and thither to attend to the various needs of the bar, the dining-room or the bedrooms. Consequently, though financially distraught to see the big ships pull out, I was, in a way, content to see them go. Once more, I mused, we could return to the normal life of the village.

Thus it was that my ire was the greater when I strolled casually through the reception area and was greeted with a blank space where the ornate fire screen, delicately sewn on a linen background and depicting a small dog created from various coloured wools, had hidden the dirty black void of the chimney from sight of the visitors. The screen had disappeared – but not only that: the precious pot had also vanished, together with the red tile that it had been secured to. Some villain had used his skill, together with a chisel and probably a small hammer, to remove the concrete that the tile was set into, and had taken not only the treasured tea pot but the tile as well.

My usually even temper flipped and for the next few days all I managed to see were female forms scuttling in different directions at my approach, never coming within tongue-lashing distance. The word had evidently gone around that it was asking for instant annihilation to engage me in any form of conversation. But time, it is truly said, is a great healer, and I soon recovered from the rage occasioned by this incident and the hotel returned to what, for Ballythread and the Pier Gate, was normal.

Eleven

I HAD MEDITATED upon the problem at some length, and had come to no conclusion as to the cause, but I put it down to some strange, unknown, magnetic force emanating from this remote speck upon the landscape of the globe that caused Ballythread to prove an irresistible attraction to a tremendous number of weird persons who, appearing and disappearing, managed to enliven the usually monotonous routine of a small fishing village.

Consequently, it was with no great surprise that I witnessed the arrival of Priam. Admittedly the memory of him lingers on, for although having seen many strange specimens perambulating along the main street, Priam was probably the strangest of all.

He arrived off the daily bus from Donegal, a tall and emaciated figure, broad of shoulder and with the lines of bygone hardships etched upon his angular face. But his main physical feature consisted of a long grey beard, neatly plaited, which hung from his jowels like a giant rat's tail to well below his navel. It was not this appendage that caused the locals to give him more than a passing glance on his arrival, however; the source of wonder lay rather in his exceptional sense of dress. He was elegantly clad in a robe of silk smothered in embroidered decorations which consisted of half moons, stars, signs of the Zodiac and some motifs too colourful and intricate to be interpreted by the casual observer. With a haughty glance of disdain at the small, gaping crowd he set off along a small road that led into the country.

In the bar that evening, his arrival was the main topic of conversation. Even the usually stoical residents were taken aback that this modern day Merlin the magician should come into their midst, and many and varied were the reasons propounded for his arrival.

Several days elapsed before he delighted the population by making another appearance. This time he strode in from the country, a large bag upon his back and, entering the local store, presented a long list of groceries that he required. He was served immediately, for all the other customers hung back to view his purchases. All were thrown casually into the bag and upon the completion of his order he demanded the bill in a very loud and harsh American accent. Somewhat worriedly Vernon calculated with the well-chewed stub of a pencil upon the back of a paper bag, this so far being the nearest that he had come to the wonders of computerization.

"It's twenty-seven pounds sixty," he finally pronounced with no great conviction.

The emaciated figure glowered down upon him and the grey beard appeared to stand out like a poker. "In dollars, boy. American dollars," he demanded.

His efforts to achieve the account in pounds had apparently exhausted Vernon's mathematical capabilities, and he looked appealingly at the rest of the customers.

"It'll be about forty dollars – you won't go far wrong at that," I piped up.

The grey beard pointed antagonistically in my direction. "No, he God damn well won't!" snarled the impressive vision. "On the bank rate this morning it would be thirty-five dollars and forty cents."

He reached into the depths of his multi-coloured robe and extracted an impressive roll of United States currency. Carefully he counted out thirty-six dollars and offered them to Vernon.

"If you don't get the account out of that I'll make it good the next time I come in," he said and, swinging the heavy bag up on his shoulder, he headed purposefully from the shop.

Fascinated, I trooped along behind him and was somewhat startled to see him enter the Pier Gate. From outside the bar I could see him engage Ann Marie in conversation, and then she went away to concoct a pint of draft Guinness for him, widely considered to be one of the best that could be obtained, presumably because the vast time that she had been practising her chosen calling had made her perfect in the construction and pouring of the pint. He squatted on a tall bar stool waiting for this beverage to be served to him. Evidently even he realized that the time involved in its creation was so that some magical and splendid transmogrification could take place in the glass before he could fittingly raise it to his lips.

Upon this potion being placed on a small cardboard beer mat in front of him, he glared balefully at Ann Marie.

"How much is that in American dollars?" he wanted to know.

"One dollar fifty," Ann Marie replied as quick as a flash.

The multi-coloured one seemed stunned by the news.

"God damn!" he wailed. "I can get the same wash in the Dock Bar for one dollar ten."

His calling upon the deity had offended the religious leanings of the redoubtable Ann Marie, and she fixed him with a steely look.

"Aren't you the bigger eejit, then," she said coldly. "Why aren't you over there drinking it?"

The plain logic of this statement apparently stumped the mystic, for he grunted and dug into one of his copious pockets. "You're all right, doll!" he exclaimed. "I'll have to think about that one."

He handed over the required dollar fifty and began to sup meditatively at his brew. Evidently it pleased him, for he had no more chat and indeed looked quite uncomfortable each time he felt Ann Marie's beady eyes fasten upon him.

However, he finished the glass with every evidence of satisfaction, picked up his purchases, and strode from the bar.

That same day the Ballythread magnet once again exerted its pulling power to attract the unusual, this time in the form of two more Americans. He was a tall, lanky individual, very much unshaven, and clad in fringed mock-buckskin raiment; he looked remarkably like a refugee from the Buffalo Bill show. His companion was just the opposite. A small plump girl, she scarcely reached his armpit though, judging from the sweat stains on his buckskin, this was probably a piece of good fortune for her. Her lack of stature was emphasized by the fact that she had one leg a good four inches shorter than the other, and her gait would have made a non-seafaring person somewhat seasick. He pretended not to notice her presence at all, and gazed at the passing throng placidly while she bounced around his waistline peering up at him with adoration. It transpired that they were in search of work and, more out of kindness than need, the owner of the local petrol pumps agreed to employ them. Over the next few days the pair became a favourite topic of conversation.

From somewhere the man had managed to obtain an old wooden rocking chair, and this he placed on the pavement each morning and settled himself comfortably, swaying gently back and forth. His girlfriend sat on the desk in the small office situated behind the pumps. Since the office was not blessed with a window she was unable to see any cars arriving, but this problem was solved by her swain letting out a stentorian bellow.

"Rhoda! Will you for Christ sake get off your ass and shoot some gas into this guy?"

The unfortunate Rhoda would then come bobbing from the office, lug the filling hose around the car and do the necessary; then, replacing the petrol cap, she would spreadeagle herself over the bonnet and give the windscreen a perfunctory rub with a damp and dirty cloth. By the time she had finished her chores he had resumed his somnolent state, and she would return to the office again.

They were never seen to eat and existed on a diet of mineral waters which she purchased from the nearby grocers, and since they made no attempt to find any sort of accommodation they slept in the office, which, it not being equipped with any sort of toilet facilities, led to widespread speculation that, since they never ate, they were also able to do without the other normal human functions.

However, while rocking his days away he was never loathe to engage passers-by in conversation, mostly in a long eulogy on the vast wonders and glories of the ranges of Texas, the huge herds of cattle, the steel forests of the countless oil rigs and the nodding metal heads of the collossal pumps as they extracted the black gold from caverns far underground. Since all these stories were expounded in a very hard New York accent and, judging from his performance in Ballythread, he had yet to soil his hands with a day's work, one was moved to wonder if he had ever visited the Lone Star State let alone rushed all over the range branding cattle or pumping oil. The locals listened politely to these revelations which, indeed, gained adornment each time they were repeated in the various hostelries by the recipients of the tales that certainly originated from no further than his fertile mind. Many and varied were the explanations put forward as to the reason that they had arrived in Ballythread, and his own freely given information that they were there "to save enough bread to buy grass" left the residents even more puzzled for, after all, wasn't the whole country covered in grass and who, in the name of Sweet Jesus, would want to swop any of it for stale bread?

It was, of course, only a matter of time before fate took a hand and, as though it were the will of Allah, the two fuel-injection technicians met Priam during one of his rare visits to town to stock up the big bag with provisions. Likewise it was only natural that they should find themselves to be kindred spirits, and after long conversation the two relinquished their abode in the petrol pump office and moved in with Priam, who had by now rented a small thatched cottage.

There matters rested, except for occasional snippets of information from the rocking chair. Priam apparently was ex-CIA and had defected; he was being avidly hunted by his colleagues, but his mystic properties enabled him to see the coming of these enemies and depart for new hiding places before their arrival. He of the rocking chair had found that their auras met together on a very high plane, which was why they had immediately become such firm friends.

I was sitting in my own office one morning when Ann Marie breezed in.

"I've ordered ten extra drums of Guinness," she announced.

It was transparently obvious that she wished me to enquire further as to the reason for this, so I obliged.

"It's the monthly mart – they has it every six weeks or so," she answered triumphantly.

"But we've had marts before, Ann Marie," I said, "and you never needed much more in the way of stock."

"Ah!" she said, "but this is the big one: all the old farmers from way back in the country bring their beasts into town and buy and sell, but mostly they use it as an excuse to get as full as an egg, so I thought that we'd better be ready for them."

The morning dawned fine and I was awakened by my beloved wife vigorously digging her bony elbow into my ribs.

"They're coming in," she hissed.

"Good luck to them," I answered sleepily. "If they find anything we'll split it fifty-fifty and we'll both be rich."

"No!" she snarled. "It's the mart. Can't you hear all the tractors?"

I sat up in the bed and cocked an ear. Sure enough, the village resounded to the roar of powerful diesel engines and the clatter of machinery, together with the bellowing of beasts and the plaintiff "baa, baa" of sheep as they were driven along, efficiently herded by the black and white sheep-dogs much favoured by the farmers who lived far back in the mountains. Reluctantly I arose from the softness and warmth of the connubial couch, and by the time that I had completed the necessary ablutions and descended to the ground floor the bar was packed with a variety of doughty characters. All were shod in well-worn wellington boots, most of which displayed malodorous traces of their travels. Rough-hewn men, all of great age, their faces were seamed and lined from many years of hard toil on the land, their hands red and chapped from continual labour in the hard weather conditions that usually prevailed.

Ann Marie was in her element, greeting each new customer

by name or nickname and enquiring of his family through to the second-cousin twice removed while at the same time filling the counter with pints of Guinness and small glasses of the amber liquid so favoured by those of the country. The bar was redolent with the smells of the farmyard, and of the turf smoke that clung to the assembly. My heart sank as I visualized the cost of shampooing all of the carpeting and furniture after they had departed, but at the same time I realized that I should be grateful for all the trade that they had brought, for each and every one of them, though their regalia looked as if it had been passed from generation to generation, seemed to have an inexhaustable stock of notes rolled tightly in the top pocket. Seemingly inexhaustable also was their thirst and even at this early hour words were beginning to be slurred, and several committed the gravest sin of all in that they began to slop their drink on the counter instead of pouring it down their throats. As the day progressed they still stood in the same places and the animals continued to make their presence felt, both by the varying noises they produced and by the increasing stench drifting downwind from where they were penned or tied. I wondered when the business of the day would take place, but at last it dawned on me that it was actually in the process.

Every so often two farmers would adjourn to the outer regions and one would expound at some length on the attributes of some unfortunate beast, while the other would mournfully announce that he would never have left his pint had he known that he was to view such a spavined-looking creature. A show of rage and indignation followed from the vendor, and the price asked and offered would close slightly until after interminable wrangling a bargain was struck and sealed by a hard slapping of hands followed by a handshake, whereupon the two would return to the bar and spend more money buying each other jars than was the difference in the last part of the heated bargaining. As the stout flowed and the whiskey glinted the patrons mellowed and stories of previous marts began to be recounted.

"Paddy, do you remember the time that old Jim from Gollmagorey was here with a rake of sheep, and he got so drunk that when he went to the auction and bid he found that he had bought his own back again?"

This sally occasioned much hilarity and loud shouts that more refreshment be provided for the raconteur.

"Aye! And remember the time that Charlie the Brook came in with that fine-looking pony of his which he was so proud of, and he spent all day trying to sell it but we thought the price was too high, and in the end that Swedish fellow up the road bought it for a tremendous sum. Well, when Charlie meets him again after a few weeks he asks him, 'Were you pleased with the pony, sir?'

"The Swedish fellow rubs his belly and smiles happily at Charlie. 'It was delicious,' he says.

"Poor old Charlie nearly choked on his Guinness. The poor man was very put out: he could speak of nothing else for weeks."

This anecdote caused howls of glee, and some of the listeners were so overcome by the humour of the situation that they slipped from their stools and hammered their fists on the bar, occasionally wiping their eyes with the caked, manure-laden sleeves of their coats.

"Arr!" piped up a wrinkled ancient sitting in the corner and resting on a fine blackthorn walking stick which apparently had a permanent resting place between his knees.

The assembly fell silent, awaiting the gems that were to come.

"What about them there Yankees that we got up in Carraweel now?"

"What about them, then?"

Seeing that he had the attention of the company the ancient located a well-smoked pipe from his pocket and lit it, causing his immediate circle of friends to go into a fit of coughing. He inhaled luxuriously.

"That funny bugger with the rat's tail hanging out of his face – he been buying sheep off of me."

"So?" asked one of the listeners.

"So, since I sees none of them a-grazing I thinks to myself, what's he doing with them? Well, one night I happened to be passing that wee cottage that he got rented and, dang me, the blare of some wierd music and chanting would near crack the wax in your ears. I thinks to myself, I'll have a peep round the back, for I could see some kind of a glow coming from there. I nips along the hedge, and would you believe, there he is a-howling and a-screaming, and those two creatures from the town with him a-joining in. They got a big fire a-roaring and there, hanging over the fire on a rack, is a sheep a-roasting. I tell you, it sent a shiver down my spine. Now I knows what he's been a-buying my sheep for, and I'll tell ye all, I'm none too pleased about it; after all, I'll put a fiver on it, he's no butcher."

I moved away. All was now crystal clear. The garage labourers had obviously found a source of grass, and it was probably their bread that the bold Priam was using to supplement his diet of fresh meat. When I informed my Tat of this discovery she was disgusted but I really thought no more about it, being far too busy assisting various gentry to navigate their ways from the bar stools, across the heaving floor and out into the open air. The shock of breathing deeply of this untainted ozone had a detrimental effect on many of them, and strong country legs that had stood up all day at the mart with the solidity of steel columns suddenly took on the appearance of boiled spaghetti and refused to bear the weight of their owners. All were duly sat on the wall within which the straggling rose bushes struggled to survive, and those that had been advised throughout the day to "get it down you – it will do you good" now reversed the advice in the faint hopes of doing better. Ann Marie appeared to obtain great satisfaction as each of the protagonists was unceremoniously carted to the door and recounted happily what she would say to them in six weeks time, at the next assembly of the monthly mart. By the time that I had managed to escort the last of these agricultural businessmen to the door it was well after closing time, and it was with a sigh of relief that I viewed the last staggering caricature of humanity reel across the Diamond and presumably depart for the wilds of the country.

I crept into the bedroom where my helpmate Tat slumbered peacefully and slid between the sheets. It had been a grand day, as it would be called in the local parlance, and, no doubt, the following day would be as good, if only we would have the health to enjoy it.

Twelve

B Y THIS TIME I had grown to know the native bush telegraph that invariably worked in Ballythread, and so at lunchtime it was no great surprise when the big Sergeant of the Guards arrived in the hotel. He squatted his ample bulk on a stool and, with no prompting, called for two pints of the black broth.

"Now, me dear," he said, after we had both quaffed deeply. "Would you tell me what in the name of God are all those queer Yanks doing up in the hills?"

"What?" I asked, pretending innocence.

"You know what," he said, peering upon me. "You were here, you heard the story. I've heard so many versions that it would make a man's head reel."

I decided that discretion was the better part of valour, and I knew that to make an enemy of the Sergeant was commonly known as the best and cheapest way of committing suicide, whether practical or financial. I retold the story that the ancient had related and, so far as I could, kept strictly to the limits of his information.

The Sergeant heaved a big sigh. He pondered deeply, sought inspiration from frequent draughts from his glass, and finally pronounced his decision.

"I suppose that what they are doing is not actually breaking the law. After all, they're only slaughtering sheep for their own consumption; but they're not going to do it on my patch, for I don't like it."

He wriggled uncomfortably on the stool and as I maintained a discreet silence he was forced to ask, "What would you do if you was faced with a similar set of circumstances?"

This direct question faced me with a problem. If our American friends had committed no offence against the law then obviously no person, sergeant or not, could do anything about it, no matter how repulsive they found these activities; but Ballythread was not an ordinary town where the strict rules of the law applied. Here the large gentleman sitting opposite me was in all but the written word the law, and he undoubtedly did not like the thought of being forced into a position where he had to watch their antics with no real recourse to the written law to end them.

"Easy," I told him.

The big man breathed a sigh of relief. "I knew you'd think of something," he said. So moved was he that he sprang to his feet and hied himself to the bar where he purchased refills even though he had paid for the first couple.

While he was away I pondered the best way to get him out of his obvious quandary, and by the time that he returned I was ready with a solution.

"All you have to do," I said softly, "is to get hold of the public health people. The man has undoubtedly not got a slaughter-house licence, the cottage will definitely not pass their regulations. You have a word with the buck before he goes up there, and when he comes down and tells you of all the infringements of the law – well, all you have to do is to go up and tell them to clear off and, if by a mischance they happen to trip over the front doorstep, well, that's their fault. Anyway, they're not thick and they'll get the general message and depart; after all, that's what you want, isn't it?"

The big platter face was wreathed in smiles. "They said you was clever," he intoned, rubbing his huge hands together. "I never would have thought of that, and I can take a swipe at the bugger before I heaves him on the bus. I'm fair fed up with all these strange sods coming into my town."

We finished our libations and he lumbered off, presumably to acquaint the Public Health Officer of his requirements.

It was a foregone conclusion as to the outcome of the affair, and the next evening the magical one, still clad in his flowing robe, was unceremoniously bundled on to the bus out of town, never to be seen again in Ballythread. The main benefit of this removal to me was that it cemented my friendship with the big Sergeant, and this was to prove advantageous in many ways.

The first time that I was able to assess the value of this friendship was when I was conned. Ambling around the hotel one day I was accosted by a customer who, in time-honoured tradition, would not converse with me in public but asked, quite politely though with an air of great mystery, if I would come out to the reception area and have speech with him. Such a request was usually a prelude to the question, "Would you mind lending me a few quid till Friday?" I therefore followed unwillingly, knowing that I'd have to make up some excuse as to why I found this impossible to do at the present time, and yet not offend him by so doing.

He slunk behind the reception desk which at this time was unattended and came out holding a long parcel wrapped in oiled brown paper. Carefully scrutinizing the area he opened the package, and there lay the most beautiful rifle that I had ever laid eyes on. A gleaming walnut stock, lethal-looking barrel of burnished steel, all brand new and, to top it off, a long telescopic sight set carefully into brackets on top of the weapon.

"I'm desperate hard-up," he announced. "This has been in the house a long time and I don't use it."

There was a pause while he allowed me to examine the gun.

"Would you be interested in making me an offer?"

I tried to keep my face straight, for he was not to know that I had for years nursed an indescribable yearning to own a rifle. The chance to own one such as this was beyond my wildest expectations. I had never shot one, but had been much impressed when I had watched more fortunate mortals stalking over the moors and highlands firing guns at grouse and pheasant and trotting home to feast on the results of their skill.

"Seems to be a reasonably decent banger," I agreed airily. "But I'm afraid it would be too expensive for me. What would you want for it anyway?"

He hesitated, seeing that I appeared to be not very interested. "I'd let it go for sixty pounds," he said.

"Then you'll have to go to someone else," I said. "I couldn't afford to shell out that type of cash when I really don't know how to fire the bloody thing."

"Fifty," he said.

"I'll risk giving you forty," I countered.

He went into an agony of concentration, seemed loathe to part with it but, finally, when I reached in to my pocket and showed him the notes, be grudgingly gave in and held his hand out.

I counted out the forty and immediately he had departed I adjourned to the office to gloat over my new acquisition – even handling it was a pleasure. I was looking upon it with pride, day-dreaming of a great safari with myself as the white hunter leading his party through thick bush in search of the man-eating tiger, when my reverie was interrupted by the arrival of my beloved wife.

"What on earth have you got there?" she demanded.

"It's a wee gun I got cheap," I answered defensively. "I thought that I'd do a bit of shooting; the exercise would get a bit of this weight off, and you've been telling me to do something about that for quite a while."

Surprisingly she agreed but administered a strict admonition.

"Before you go off firing that thing you'd better go up to the barracks and get a licence."

I had not contemplated that such a requirement would be necessary but I kept my face straight.

"Of course," I replied haughtily. "Wouldn't dream of using the thing until I was covered."

She must have been busy because she left it at that, so, clasping my treasure, I strode up the road to the guardian of the law's den. Here I found the Sergeant slumped behind a desk far too small for his bulk. He greeted me warmly, but then his face changed as he viewed the long black barrel that stuck out in front of me as I cradled the gun in my arms.

"Holy Jesus!" he exclaimed. "Where did you come upon that thing?"

Proudly I told him of the offer I could not possibly have refused.

"You bloody fool," he announced. "Do you not know that that is a Magnum gun. We've not allowed anyone to own one of them since the troubles in the North. The damn things are lethal, man. You could kill up to a mile with one of them, and anyway, nobody would sell you any ammunition for it unless you produced a special permit. I'm supposed to impound any that I find, but there's none left now."

"Oh God!" I moaned. "I've been conned. What's more, I never saw the fellow before in my life. I bet he's having a good laugh somewhere."

The law officer shifted in the chair. "We'll see if we can get him to laugh on the other side of his face," said he. Reaching into one of the drawers of the desk he retrieved a paper volume, yellowed with age, and studied it carefully.

"Ah!" he said proudly. "I knew I'd seen it someplace. How would you like to be the official mad-dog shooter for Bally-thread and district?"

"Are there any mad dogs?" I enquired with some disquiet.

"Never seen one yet," he said. "But we must comply with the law."

Having delivered himself of that profound statement he again rummaged in the drawer and soon I had my signature on a form that made me the official shooter, though fortunately both for my sake and for the sake of the locals in the town it did not come to pass that I ever had to show my prowess in this particular way.

Thirteen

THROUGH THIS AND many other instances I discovered that the law in Ireland was respected by all and sundry, provided that it did not in any way interfere with something that they particularly wished to do. Then it was waived with a gay nonchalance and, provided you managed to get away with whatever nefarious project you contemplated, the remainder of the people would comment admiringly on your artistry.

So it was during the salmon season. The rules concerning the catching of the silver kings of the sea were strict and, in addition to the Gardaí who kept a watchful eye on the rivers, there were the bailiffs who, travelling in ordinary cars and out of uniform, tried to make life as difficult as possible for the poachers. The poachers existed in great numbers and after dusk were to be seen scampering down the banks of the river swathed in rolls of pink or green polypropelene net which they carefully set above and below the numerous river pools. As a result the unfortunate fish had an even more hazardous journey as they made their way up to their spawning grounds.

With a haul secured, these gentlemen would appear at the door of the kitchen, peer upon me with a conspiratorial expression, and motion for me to follow them. The boot of an ancient car would be half opened and the catch of the night would lie before me on the floor. Bargaining was swift for the locals knew the price the fish were making on the Dublin market from day to day, so that a rough buying price was already in existence before the bargaining began. On my part, since the fines for being found with poached fish in a hotel were savage, I only wanted as many as could be quickly grilled and sold, in which case the fact that it was illegal fish was difficult to prove; on the other hand, the sellers were looking for a market for their complete catch for, once having unloaded it, they too were safe to continue on their way. Luckily I always managed to have my stock eaten before the bailiffs arrived to look through the freezers and cold room.

The nearest we came to being caught was when a bailiff appeared in Reception shortly after an arrangement had been reached with a gentleman who had done exceedingly well on the river the night before and, in addition to three or four salmon, had a goodly number of the greatly prized river trout as well. I had not resisted the temptation and had purchased them all. When the bailiff stood before me my heart fell – I had been caught! Offering up an unaccustomed prayer I greeted the bailiff with a smile and announced that I had nothing to do with the kitchen but, if he would wait a few moments, I would procure the services of my lady wife who would be only too pleased to show him the various fridges and freezers.

Casually I sauntered into the bar, then, when out of his sight, I rushed into the kitchen. Catch and a couple of the girls were there.

"Drop everything," I hissed. "It's the bailiffs! Get all of the fish out of the freezers and dump it in the spare room at the end of the yard."

The girls scampered in and out like jack rabbits and within minutes the deadly evidence was away and I produced Tat, who chatted nicely to the bailiff as he peered into the recently brimming fridges and freezers.

This episode shook me and for a while I managed to evade the lure of cheap fish but, like everyone else in the business, now and again I'd be tempted, for it is a true saying that forbidden fruit tastes better.

I was relating this anecdote in the Holly Leaf a few days later and naturally great mirth was aroused by the antics. However, as so often happens, one story led to another, and this time it was Charlie Byrne who took up the cudgels.

"Do you remember Desperate Harry?" he asked the assembled imbibers.

A chorus in the affirmative greeted him and several crossed themselves and delivered themselves of the hope that he was happy, from which I deduced that the said Desperate had shuffled off this mortal toil.

"Well," said Charlie, tamping his pipe well down and drawing a malodorous cloud of smoke into his lungs. "It was when old McNulty was the District Justice – you all remember him, a baldy headed bugger and very hard on a man if he didn't like the face of him. A man very fond of fresh fish he was. Each time he arrived in Ballythread for to sit on the court he would see to it that somebody managed to get a few nice plaice or, if he was lucky, a big black sole for him to take home for his tea. Well, Desperate had been caught by the Gardaí for having an old beer bottle label stuck in his car window instead of a tax disc, and up to the bench he was going. But before the court old McNulty always called in at the hotel for a tray of tea, and it was there that Desperate lay in wait. He somehow managed to get him alone and whispered to the effect that he might be able to liberate a nice fresh salmon, and should he place the fish in the back of the judicial car? Of course, old McNulty said that would be fine and thanked Desperate no end for his kindness."

Charlie realized he had the undivided attention of his audience, and blew out a cloud of smoke.

"Well, off goes Desperate to the pier, and there stands a truck with about twenty or more boxes of fresh salmon all packed up and on their way to the market in Dublin.

Desperate lifts the canvas and grabs a good ten-pounder, slips it under his jacket and hops back across the Diamond. He makes sure that the Justice sees him placing it in the boot of his car, then off he goes to court.

"Of course, when Desperate's case comes up, McNulty announces that it is a crying shame that a man would remove a tax disc from another man's car and put a beer label in its place; it just goes to show, he says, the depths of general blackguarding and theft that was sweeping the country. He dismissed the case and called for the next."

General laughter broke out as he apparently completed his story, but he waved us to silence with a sweep of the stem of his pipe.

"Wait!" he cried. "You haven't heard the best part of it yet! Desperate knew that one of the men on the pier had seen him slinking off with the fish, so he nips back down the street, gets it out from the back of the Justice's car, and carts it back down the pier again. He waves it at the fellow who saw him. 'There,' he says. 'Blast your eyes, never say I stole one fin off of you; I just borrowed the wee sprat for a short while in a good cause,' and he puts it back in the box and takes off down the road. I guess the Justice is still wondering where his nice salmon tea went to!"

Amid the laughter a new wave of the black beverage was produced and another hardy looking customer took up the position of the storyteller.

"Aye!" he said. "And do you remember the time that the same fellow passed through the kitchen of the Pier Gate on his journeying around the town – that was afore you were there," he added, addressing me.

"He clears the door when the old cook that they had then notices that a complete, newly cooked ham had gone from its resting place on the kitchen table. The old bag heads after Desperate like a whippet and comes up on him just as he's making for the main door. There he is, looking for all the world like one of those Mafia gangsters, his hand in under his coat and the old cap pulled down over his eyes. 'Why, hello, Harry,' says she, sticking out her hand as if to shake his, but, of course, Desperate can't, for he has the ham, still warm, clasped to him under his raincoat. She ups to him in a flash and before he can do a thing she wraps herself around him like some kind of big snake and rubs herself around him like some foolish girl on her first date. Poor Desperate, he was mortified. There he was feeling all the fat and juices running down inside his trousers and unable to say a word against it. First time ever that he was stuck for words. Finally she gives up. 'There you are,' she says, 'I hope that you enjoyed that more than you're going to enjoy getting the mess off of your clothes'."

It appeared that the stories relative to the activities of Desperate were numerous but, much as I was enjoying the company, I decided that I must return to the Pier Gate and see if there was anything going on there.

I thought at first that there might be for the Sergeant was resting on the front window-sill, but he made no move as I parked the car. I crossed the pavement and sat beside him.

"Been to the Leaf?" he asked.

I nodded assent.

"A nice pub. I suppose all the usual lunch-time crowd were there?"

"Yes," I replied. "I'm getting to know most of them now. They were telling stories about some fellow that they called Desperate."

"Ho!" he wheezed. "A bigger crook never set foot in the district, but likeable with it. He got up to some rare capers, but I never really had much cause to go after him; mostly it was between him and his unfortunate neighbours. It was him, you know, that sold the house to that Yankee family that have settled down on the point. A right killing he made there."

"Yes," I replied. "I've heard of them, but they seem to keep very much to themselves; I never see them in the town and, far as I know, they've never been in the hotel, either to eat or even have a jar."

"No," he replied. "You wouldn't. Ever since they got here and bought the place they've been having the very devil of a time trying to make the house fit for anyone to live in."

He struggled into a more comfortable position on the hard sill and continued.

"Poured money into it even faster than the water that pours through the roof. But the man's a trier. He employed the biggest crowd of idle blackguards in the district to make repairs to the place and they bled him white, so he started doing some of it himself. Still, I hear that he isn't as good at doing things as he thinks he is. For instance, there was the chimney that he built."

"I'd not heard about that," I said. "But I had heard that he was some kind of wierdo."

The big man chuckled. "Aye! But I suppose that he got the better of us with the chimney; it depends on which way you look at it."

He lit a cigarette and puffed happily.

"He had a yen for one of those stone fire-places, the same as you see in the old country places, so he ordered a pile of that nice coloured stone from the quarry up there in Meenahanna and went to work. Tore up the floors, smashed down the wall, and eventually had a hole that ran from the ground floor to the roof. And them living in the place all the time! Then he started to build the fire-place and chimney. Worked like a dog, he did, and finally the great day came and it was finished. He dragged in some logs and had a waggon-load of turf, and they sat down to enjoy the fire.

"Well," he cackled with glee, "you never saw the like of it. Smoke poured out from between every brick, into the bedrooms above, and in the room where they were sitting you could have smoked fish."

"How could that possibly have happened?" I asked innocently.

"He arrived in the Leaf the next day, and he asked the very same question," said the Sergeant.

"It turned out that he'd put no liner at all on the inside of the chimney, just built it up with stones. He asked what the hell he could do. A few of the boys were there and they told him he'd have to rip the thing down, start again, and put in the liner as he went up. He digests this information while he's finishing his pint, then up he hops and out he goes, and no one sees him for at least a week. One day he appears in the Fisherman's Bar and gets himself set up on a bar stool. He orders a pint and a wee half and looks pretty broody while he's sipping it. Since he looked a little worse for wear the barmaid felt a bit sorry for him, so she asks him how things are going down at the house. 'These God-damn Irish,' he said, 'they don't know nothing.' He tells her the story of how, with his own bare hands, he erected the chimney, and now he was told that the only cure would be to rip it down. 'Lot of bullshit,' he announced. 'All you need is a little intelligence.'"

"How did he do it then?" I asked, for it was the only reasonable solution to the problem that I could think of.

The Sergeant chuckled again. "Well, as he told it, he got his 'broad' and the kids outside, and he climbs on the roof. He's got a pile of mixed lining compound lying on a board in the grate, and he takes a length of rope up on the roof with him. This he ties around his ankles, then sticks his skull down the chimney. The poor wife and the kids then lower him down the chimney head first. By and by he gets to the grate and he ties the board with the lining compound round his neck. He's got a trowel and he goes round the inside of the chimney with the compound. Each time he lets out a roar the wife and the kids heave on the rope and he goes up a little bit higher. After the full week was over, bless my soul, hadn't he got the whole thing lined from the inside."

He paused for breath. "No wonder he looked a little the worse for wear."

I looked at him incredulously. "You're having me on?" I said.

"On my mother's grave," he insisted. "True as I'm sitting here."

I was quite prepared to sit all afternoon and listen to his reminiscences, but my pleasure was interrupted by the arrival of my beloved Tat.

"The well is overflowing," she said.

Had there been any sun, I would have surmised that she had spent too much time in it.

"We don't have a well," I said patiently. "We are on the mains – for what they're worth."

"The dining-room is built over the old well," she pronounced slowly, as though explaining some simple information to a child. "It must be blocked," she continued, "because the water is welling up through the dining-room floor. You'll have to do something or we'll not be able to open tonight."

I leapt from the sill and followed her scurrying figure up the hall. My worst forebodings were confirmed, and so was the truth in her statement. The dining-room, a large area all beautifully covered with mock parquet flooring, was shining as if it had just been polished. However, this effect was achieved by the fact that about a quarter of an inch of water had found its way upwards from some hidden source.

"Who, in the name of Allah, would be so stupid as to build a dining-room over a well?" I asked.

"My mother," Tat replied acidly.

The rotund figure of Ann Marie appeared, her face wearing an expression that portended imminent doom.

"Always said she'd rue the day she built over a spring well," she announced heavily.

I felt a slight stirring of hope within me.

"Who built it, Ann Marie?" I asked urgently. "If we could get hold of them we might find out if they made any allowance for overflow – there must be a pipe some place that is supposed to carry the excess water away."

"It was the Kiernans of Weelin," she replied. "Very good workmen they were."

I had discovered that anyone that came from Weelin was a confirmed expert and as honest as the day was long, according to Ann Marie.

"Where can I phone them?" I asked, trying not to convey the feeling of disaster that I felt.

"Can't," she said. "Poor Tommy – God rest his soul, I hope he's happy – passed away just after the job was completed."

My expression must have told her that I was out for the count as far as further ideas were concerned.

"But," she began again, looking down at the carpet in the hallway, "I always thought that there was a man-hole under here somewhere, and I think I remember Tommy rooting in it while they were here and saying that the spill would have to go down there to the new drain."

She was scarcely finished speaking before I was pulling at the carpet in the place she had indicated. Sure enough, tucked neatly under the carpet felt was a small iron cover. Of course, as is always the case with such things, it refused to budge at first but once persuaded with a length of iron bar I was able to look into the hole beneath. Further searching on my part revealed some drain rods and, with a prayer to I knew not whom, I thrust one after the other up the pipe that led in the direction of the dining-room.

For at least six rods' lengths nothing happened, then the rod came up against some obstruction. I shoved frantically, twisting and turning the rods, and at last a gurgling noise echoed down the pipe.

"I think you've got him now," said Ann Marie.

I withdrew the rods and the three of us peered down the hole as if awaiting the second coming.

What eventually came up left us speechless. Like an ice-skater gracefully gliding across the rink an ancient wellington boot slid from the pipe and flopped into the retaining pit. The appearance of this article was signal for a veritable cascade of water to gush from the pipe. Frothing and splashing it rushed into the opposite pipe and vanished down under the hall, heading, I was relieved to note, in the direction of the outside pavement.

"Go and look in the dining-room," I told Tat, who was squatting on her hunkers beside me.

She must have been equally moved by the sight, for she left to do my bidding without a word of remonstration.

"It's stopped," she shouted from the dining-room doorway, "and it's running away from the floor."

I retrieved the offending boot and, so that the story could be relayed with adequate proof, stored it in a shed in the yard. I mentally blessed the memory of Ann Marie and placed the iron lid back in the opening. I felt that I had done my duty for the day, and I noticed that even my dear Tat looked upon me with favourable regard; with undying hope I trusted that such favourable regard would extend until, and after, we were tucked between the sheets.

It was the work of a moment to relay the carpet, but I made a mental note that, unless the genius from Weelin happened to be one-legged, the other boot would, over the course of the years, reappear. We had not heard the last of the spring well.

Fourteen

CATERING TO THE wishes of the eating public is not an easy task. The dining-room was always something of a nightmare but, compared to the minor day-to-day tragedies, far worse was to come. It began in a most serene manner with the arrival of a well-dressed gentleman and his wife. They asked to meet me and it transpired that he was a college professor from a university in the North. He exuded charm and showered compliments on the establishment, my wife – whom he found delightful – myself, and the staff in general.

By this time I was beginning to know a little more about the hotel business, and I patiently waited for the inevitable punch-line. Sure enough, it was not long in coming. He wished, he stated, to bring parties of thirty or forty student teachers on field courses in the vicinity and the Pier Gate would suit them very nicely as a base for their operations. Naturally, however, the students were not overburdened with money and, if we could come to an arrangement regarding suitable rates, then he might be able to convince the university authorities to use the place on a regular basis with, as he was at great pains to point out, numerous advantages to me since the bar trade would undoubtedly go up and in addition the rooms would be fully booked. We haggled for some time, but after a few whiskeys and more pints an arrangement was hammered out.

There the matter rested until, a week or so after, I was summoned to the phone and there, as though speaking from the surface of the moon, was the professor. He announced without preamble, for he must have been howling his head off even to be heard at all, that he and his wife, together with the Dean of the University and his lady, would be arriving on Friday evening so that the Dean could make a final decision as to the suitability of the premises. He further pointed out that some slight display of generosity on my part might well be to my advantage. Thus on Friday Tat personally made sure that a table for four was set up with the finest crockery, crystal glasses from our private collection and a fresh flower array, and all was prepared for the arrival. We had sliced some smoked salmon, chilled a few bottles of sparkling wine, and the cook had been told to spare nothing to see that their first meal was a success.

The evening came and, with it, the Dean, the professor, and their respective wives. We all adjourned to the bar, my Tat dressed in her finery to create the right impression, and I pumped several large libations into them as the evening got off to a great start, mutual admiration being the keynote of our encounter.

Eventually food was suggested and, after much consultation of the menu, each made their choice. Having done my bit I retired, and my beloved bustled around in the kitchen with Catch seeing that all was prepared to their satisfaction. I was pleased to note that their table was in a secluded corner of the room and that there were no other customers in at the time. The background speakers played soft music, the candles on the table flickered attractively, and the flowers looked charming as a centre display. The four sat down, and the waitresses were able to concentrate on their needs to the full.

Seeing that all was running so smoothly I thought it a good time to saunter across the road to the Fisherman's Bar where I perched myself on a stool and sucked on a quiet pint. Mentally I was patting myself on the back for securing what I was sure would be a most profitable contract. Time passed before I eventually returned, quite sure that I should be met with a fulsome accolade for the quality of the meal and the service.

I peeped into the kitchen: the cook sat with a numb look on her face while the waitresses huddled in a little group in the corner. My beloved Tat leaned against one of the cookers and seemed as if she might burst into tears at any moment.

"My God!" I turned to them. "What in the world has gone wrong?"

Tat turned a pained expression upon me.

"You'll never believe it," she whispered. "And of course you couldn't be found when we needed you."

"What happened?" I moaned.

The cook took up the tale.

"Well, they had just finished their meal, and they all said it was excellent. The whole thing had gone off really well, and they ordered brandy with their coffee. Then Barney Green, who fishes with Ted, arrived, steamed out of his mind. Well gone, he was, so the girls put him at a table at the far end of the dining-room and he managed to slur out that he wanted a T-bone and chips. Well, I put it on for him and all was well, and the next thing we know is all kinds of screams from the dining-room. We rushed to the door to see what was wrong, and there he was."

"What was he doing?" I asked softly.

"He must have dozed off for a little, and when he woke he didn't realize where he was, for there he was, his zip down and him peeing all over the middle of the floor, with your four important friends just sitting there as though paralyzed watching him – and he seemed to go on for ever. In the end Margaret managed to grab a hold of him and we threw him out, but Lord knows what your friends must have thought."

"What can we do?" moaned by beloved wife.

My mind was a blank. "Where are they now?" I gasped. "Have they left?"

"No," said one of the waitresses, "they're in the bar."

Like a snail with severe arthritis I wended my way to the bar. They had to be faced, though no amount of brilliant thought or talk could undo the event. Tentatively I crept in, and there round a table were the famous four deep in conversation.

Howls of laughter greeted my appearance.

"My God!" said the professor. "Here is the Entertainments Manager himself! Sit down and have a jar – after that performance I should think you need one."

I grasped at the straw that he had thrown me.

"I was away trying to arrange an encore," I croaked hollowly. "But the performer seems to have run short of the main feature of his act."

Much laughter greeted this sally, and the Dean waved to the barmaid who obligingly brought a round of drinks over to the table. Animated conversation followed, all trying to vie with each other as to the best way that the story could be told on their return home. As time went by and round followed round they became even more mellow, and by the time the bar closed we were in happy harmony, so much so that even my beloved Tat came over and joined the company, and in spite of her embarrassment was rapidly put at ease.

So it was that the university contract was won. We awaited the arrival of the first group of students with confidence, for even I was forced to admit that nothing worse could go wrong, no matter what type of people they were. Even the offending wretch, Barney Green, was suprised at the mildness of his greeting when he staggered in the next morning, holding his head and practically weeping as he begged forgiveness for his appalling act.

Fifteen

THROUGHOUT MANY YEARS of marriage I had discovered that many and varied were the requirements of my beloved. As each new craze hit her, obtaining her desire became the most important thing in her life, and for me life became increasingly fraught until she had achieved her goal. So it was with considerable alarm that I saw her perusing the local paper with far more concentration than was her usual wont and excitedly discussing some pronouncement within it with a group of the girls.

"Look!" she said triumphantly, waving the paper at me as I entered the room. "There is a man down in Wicklow that has wolfhound puppies for sale."

"Great news," I retorted. "Who do we know that needs one of those?"

Even before she answered I knew with a sick feeling what she was going to say.

"We do!" she exlaimed. "Just imagine: he would be such an

asset to the hotel. The Americans would come for miles to see a genuine Irish wolfhound, and he could be fed from the scraps from the dining-room so he wouldn't cost a thing to keep and, as for all those smelly old wild cats in the yard, he'd soon chase them away. I think that it's a great idea."

A chorus of assent greeted these words and my few remarks as to the exercising of the beast and where it was to take up residence were completely disregarded. I was aware that I was fighting a rearguard action; nevertheless I tried my best to dissuade her from actually putting this latest scheme into practice. But just six days later it was with little surprise that I found myself sitting in the car, Tat sitting in the passenger seat, with a look of satisfied delight wreathing her features as we set off on the journey of some one hundred and eighty miles to the home of he who had the hounds for sale.

In Ireland many of the roads are bad, some so narrow that, but for that they are infrequently used they would undoubtedly produce scenes of carnage. We appeared to wend our way down mile after mile of such tracks in our search for the magic address that Tat clasped to her bosom. Enquiries for directions from the few members of the local population that we passed evoked answers that either led us miles out of our way or resulted in our arrival at some small dead-end farmyard, where we were greeted with curiosity and a new set of directions. Finally, more by good luck than good instruction, we came upon a village and to both of us it was a complete surprise to find that we had reached the desired location.

I climbed out and stretched my legs. The village was tiny but the green in the centre was mown and well-tended and surrounded with a sprinkling of small shops. Enquiries at one of these elicited the information that the famous breeder of the wolfhounds happened to be the parish priest and that he was selling the puppies because his advancing age made them too much of a handful for him. I should have smelt a rat even then, for when a parish priest has to sell possessions that could equally well have been looked after by a few of his loyal parishioners, then something must be a little wrong. But in the wake of a joyful Tat I reluctantly dragged my feet in the direction of a large house adjoining the church at the end of the village. We entered the garden through a rough-hewn gate, decorated incongruously with liberal festoons of chicken wire; in fact, practically everything in sight was protected by similar coils of wire. It was just as we were approaching the stout front door that my instinct informed me that we were not alone. Casually I peeped over my shoulder, and promptly beat the world record for the standing high-jump.

Padding softly up the path towards us were two beasts. Dogs? I thought not. Possibly a cross between a lion and a donkey. The parish priest was obviously a raving lunatic and an admirer of the creator of the legendary Frankenstein. Their mouths were open, displaying rows of huge ivory fangs; the mind boggled at what they might do if their owners took a dislike to some person, or even another animal.

"Christ!" I croaked, and my beloved looked back as well.

"Oh! They're lovely," she squealed and headed off back down the path towards them. My warning shout was ignored as she hurled herself upon the larger of the two animals. I use the word "upon" advisably, for the brute was certainly larger than herself. However, it seemed not to mind being leapt on by this strange creature, and as my wife stroked its half acre of back she was rewarded by having half a yard of tongue dragged across her face. This action caused her to nearly expire with delight.

Our arrival must have been detected from within for, as I watched half in fear and half in fascination while my beloved tempted death with the animals, the front door opened and a woman of some seventy years of age appeared. She was wiping her hands on a none-too-clean cloth.

"Good day," she greeted me politely. "The Father is taking a small nap at the moment. Were you wanting something?"

"Well," I hesitated. "We saw that you had some wolfhound pups for sale and thought that we might take a look at them, but I guess these aren't the ones?" I gestured at the huge beasts which were now gazing solemnly upon us and swishing their tails.

"No, no," she chuckled. "They are the parents; the tiny ones are round here at the back."

She set off and my wife and I trailed behind her. The yard looked like a battlefield. It boasted two battered-looking wooden structures which, presumably, were meant to be kennels but looked more like small garden sheds; spread over the ground was a profusion of multi-coloured washing-up bowls, each with a liberal portion of some foul-looking gruel adhering to the sides. Leaping in, over and around these were some of the strangest-looking animals I had ever set eyes on. It was difficult to comprehend that these small creatures dragging long spindly tails upon the ground would ever grow up to be like the giants that panted behind us.

Once again Tat went into raptures: reaching down she commenced to fondle one of the yelping progeny. She appeared not to care that the creature was liberally coated in mud, gruel and what else I shuddered to think. It was difficult to count because of the constant movement, but I deduced that there were six of the small ones, give or take one either way. They rushed around the woman who was clasping one of their number and wiped their furry bodies happily against her legs. All the while she uttered dulcet cooing sounds which I deduced were intended to convey friendship to the wriggling object clutched in her arms.

The old woman, who evidently looked after and "did" for the venerable parish priest, looked on with a benign expression as my female idiot moved from one struggling pup to the next, making a fuss of each in his or her turn and getting more smeared with the mud and gruel mixture as she did so. Each smelly object was duly praised for a variety of reasons that I completely failed to see and finally, all having received their fair share of affection, the woman asked if we would care to partake of a pot of tea and wait until the priest would awake and we could discuss the purchase with him himself.

Hastily I declined the offer on the pretext that I should prefer to take a stroll and stretch my legs after the long drive down, but my beloved accepted with alacrity and I realized that she had no intention of being parted from the swarming horde or the two giant beasts until being forced to do so. I departed rapidly, pleased to note that I was not followed by either the parents or the litter, and made my way back to the village green. Memory had served me correctly and one of the small shops also boasted a sign that announced that there was a bar and lounge within. I was delighted to find that the bar was clean and neat, all was highly polished, though the place had stood for many years without the addition of any adornments. Two or three elderly men sat around the fireplace, where no fire was lit as yet and, as was the inevitable practice, they ceased talking upon my entry and peered at me with deep suspicion. The owner of the shop also tended the bar and within minutes I was looking approvingly at a splendid pint. He engaged me in conversation and, since I had become resigned to the inevitable, I passed him a précis of my life history and finished up by informing him as to why I had arrived at his splendid hostelry.

There was a subdued titter from the fireplace as I came to that part of the story.

"Why?" I asked innocently. "Are the dogs no good?"

After much shuffling of feet one of the drinkers elected to answer.

"No," he said, mulling over his words with care. "The dogs is all right, 'cept as they can't keep the buggers in. Put up enough wire to serve a good-sized farm, the Father did, but chicken wire don't stop them things. Either they just push it down or they jump over it, and some of the women here are that scared of the brutes they drop all and run off if they see one coming."

"That's good news," I said. "So long as they are all right. My wife wants one and if she gets her way, and she will, there will be one less for your women to worry about."

Perhaps it was that thought that made them more friendly, for another cleared his throat.

"Fetch a tidy price, them sort of dogs," he stated. "The Father is a shrewd businessman for all of his sacred calling but he's getting rather old and very feeble, so I'm thinking that he will be glad to be getting rid of them."

Their conversation turned to ewes, and so I partook of another glass to balance the body, then made my way back to the large house.

My beloved and the old woman were getting along in a most friendly fashion and I was informed that we were about to become the proud owners of the pick of the litter and, what was more, it was a male. At this I heaved a sigh of relief, being thankful for small mercies, for at least it meant that the hotel would not be swarming with the shaggy beasts as the years rolled by.

The animated chatter of the two women was suddenly interrupted by a peculiar groaning and knocking that appeared to be coming from the corridor. The old woman leapt up, once again cleaning her hands on the grime-covered apron, and headed for the door.

"It's himself," she hurled back over her shoulder.

She returned slowly with a hunched and tottering figure clad in clerical vestments that hung from his emaciated body like an oversized black dressing-gown. The old woman clung to his right arm and he supported his left side on a blackthorn stick that was big enough to hold up a giant. Wheezing and grunting he shuffled into the room and was duly manoeuvered into a large wooden chair that stood near the window. He peered out of this for some little while as he recovered from the effort of movement, then turned to us and displayed a set of appallingly bad teeth as he smiled in our direction.

The housekeeper ran to fetch tea, and all the while she recounted to him the reason for our visit.

He considered us gravely. "They're fine dogs," he declared. "Can't let one go unless I'm sure that it will be going to a good home."

Tat burbled like a flowing brook and assured him that the animal would be treated like a king, fed on the finest of food, be cosseted like a child and, in short, become the light of her life.

The old priest considered these facts as she continued to talk and finally, when she paused for breath, he spoke.

"Come very expensive, they do," he intoned.

It was at this point that I thought I should be heard.

"What sort of money were you thinking of?" I asked.

"Since you can evidently keep him well I'd let him go for a hundred pounds." He looked warily at me from under lowered lids; in fact, he looked as if he might well drop off to sleep at any moment.

I rose to my feet. "I'm very sorry," I said, trying to put the necessary grief into my voice, "but that's far too high for me: I'd been thinking around about sixty as a maximum."

120

My beloved shot me a glance of such hatred that I nearly emulated Lot's wife and turned into a pillar of salt.

The cleric passed into a period of even deeper contemplation, then, making us all jump with surprise, he banged the huge stick on the floor.

"Make it seventy and he's yours," he said.

"Fair enough," I answered. "I suppose I can stretch to the extra ten pounds."

Thus the deal was done and we became the proud owners of a particularly filthy scrap of a dog. All was delight from the viewpoint of one member of the family, though I was delivered of a lecture, outlining to me how she had been mortified to hear me actually bargaining with a man of the cloth.

The pup was then duly transported back to Ballythread and became the object of much affection from all members of the staff. Indeed, after Tat had lovingly washed the grime from him, and he had been watered and fed and a small cot mattress procured for him to take his ease upon, even I became quite fond of the little fellow.

Sixteen

WINTER CAME UPON us with surprising sudden-
ness. One day a cold wind began to blow, then rain
blanketed the village for days on end; the wind
increased, showers of hail were interspersed with snow, and
the dreary time was upon us.

The fishing boats were tied up for weeks at a time as the
waves crashed on to the rocks at the entrance to the harbour,
and fine salt spray smeared all the windows no matter how
many times the girls tried to wash it off. As the weather
worsened it became harder and harder to keep a reasonable
degree of warmth within the fabric of the old building. Profits
gained through hard work during the tourist season were
rapidly frittered away as gallons and gallons of fuel oil
vanished into the large tank set in the back yard. I began to
think that judging by the size of the hotel's electricity bill I
must be keeping every light and cooker in the village going.
My feeling of despondency was matched only by that of the

fishermen who, as the festive season approached, became increasingly concerned that they would be unable to put to sea and make a little money with which to greet Santa on his arrival. All in all it was a very tense time and I began to realize that it was the elements, and not the will of the men, that made or broke a small fishing community.

The frightful deluge continued to lash from the heavens and the bar takings dropped as the money ran out; the trade in the dining-room became increasingly sparse as the locals took to eating at home rather than spending their savings by going out for meals. I became adept at leaping into shop doorways whenever the poker face of the bank manager appeared on the streets, and it was with a definite feeling of relief that I observed the wind fall away a few weeks before Christmas and saw all the boats rush out to sea again.

They were in luck and struck shoals of herring – the "silver darlings", harbingers of prosperity. A few buyers appeared like magic and stayed in the hotel, and so it was that I was able to soldier on into the New Year and offer up thanks that we had been saved by the bell.

It was during this period of merriment and great festivity that I discovered two peculiar characteristics of Ballythread. The first was that, far from being rushed off our feet on Christmas Eve and on Christmas Day, the village became deadly quiet. Few were to be seen on the streets and the busy piers became devoid of human life. This phenomenon was explained by the fact that most of the lads that fished on the boats came from different places across the country, and after a monumental binge for a few days before Christmas Eve they all wended their way to their respective homes there to celebrate the good tidings in a more sober atmosphere. Furthermore, the local fishermen seemed to be so fatigued after accompanying their far-flung colleagues on their binge that they rested, so that they too might fight down the mandatory turkey and ham at the appointed time.

All this unusual activity and inactivity mingled with the second strange fact that seemed peculiar to Ballythread. It transpired that it was customary for the publicans to stand a free drink to each of their customers to celebrate this festive period and in the run-up to the actual time the bar was invaded by a constant stream of new faces, each one adamant that he drank in the Pier Gate, and there only, throughout the year. This instance was a prelude to the publican having to put up a Christmas drink when the time arrived. Then, by a strange coincidence, the face that had once tipped a bottle of Guinness down its throat immediately became famished for the want of brandy, and with an air of injured innocence would hotly insist that he very rarely drank anything other than the best. This, of course, made the profits look a little thin, but I was assured by the wisdom of Ann Marie that if these drinks were not set up any chance of ever seeing the intended recipient again were slight at best. I refrained from the obvious answer that since we had never seen them before anyway it would not much matter. However, the custom persisted, and it was with some degree of alarm that after the festivities were over and the crews of the boats arrived back in Ballythread again, they all, without exception, on arrival in the bar demanded the Christmas drink that they had missed because they had been away for the duration of the celebrations. This demand continued well into January, and it was here that the vast experience of Ann Marie came to the rescue.

She would stand behind the bar, a determined expression on her face, wagging her finger at some supplicant.

"Now, now, John-Joe, you're a blackguard. Don't I remember myself giving you a large one before you left. Had it not been for the time of the year I'd not have served you for you were as drunk as a bow-legged chicken at the time, and that's why you can't remember getting it. How you never fell into the tide is a mystery to me."

An expression of deep grief and regret would come over his face, and he would earnestly insist that he could not remember, and that she should never think that he would have asked for another had he been able to recall the incident. He would then wait patiently until Ann Marie went off duty and try his luck with the barmaid that relieved her, but the girls, wise to the ways of the fishermen, would protest vigorously that they were now unable to oblige the wretch since Ann Marie would scalp them if she found out, she being in sole charge of dispensing the Christmas drink.

The whole charade was played out with completely straight

faces, and I realized that it was not so much the actual drink in question that the fishermen required, but the satisfaction of knowing that they had managed to put one over on the publican who, after all, made far too much profit out of them throughout the year, and that therefore it was a charity to try to relieve him of some of his ill-gotten gains whenever the opportunity arose.

Meanwhile I viewed with alarm the rapidly increasing size of our new little pet, who had been christened Cullen after the mythical Irish giant. Basking in the undying love of my Tat, and under the ministrations of all the girls, he lived on the fat of the land. Each and every scrap returned from the dining-room disappeared down his gullet as if he were a mobile garbage disposal unit. In addition liberal quantities of calcium for his teeth and bones and gallons of cod liver oil for his coat were thrust into him. Each day his huge paws seemed to be moving away from his body, and his tail, once dragging on the ground, now swished the air like some Arab whip.

But as he grew I noticed that the enthuasiasm the staff had shown him was fading noticeably for, in order to obtain attention, he developed the habit of thrusting his head underneath their skirts and jerking it violently upwards. The coldness of his nose in this particular area caused great distress to the waitresses in particular, especially when they were attempting to reach the dining-room with a full load of plates stacked up on their arms. Likewise, the cook found that he was soon able to look over the preparation table and would select some choice viand and slink away with it to some remote corner to devour it in comfort. I often wondered, if rescued before this time, whether Catch wiped it off and sent it on its way to some unsuspecting diner, but I did not like to ask.

Having survived the worst that winter could throw at us, and having managed to keep the maintenance men in full employment for much of that time, it was with infinite relief that, with a slight warmth in the prevailing wind, spring was heralded. I realized that we had now been in Ballythread for nearly a year.

This fact was confirmed for me when I arrived in Reception one morning and saw a lone figure peering out the window at

126

the unceasing drizzle. He was clad in a shirt decorated with reclining nubile ladies which would have been more suitable for a warmer climate, and he wore a multi-coloured flat cap pulled down firmly on his head. It was our American friend returning for his annual pilgrimage to the village.

"Hello, Jo. Nice to see you again."

He regarded me with curiosity.

"You still here?" he asked or, rather, stated. "I thought you would have got sense and taken off. Has it stopped raining since I left?"

"We had a pretty good summer," I replied. "But the winter was just dreadful."

At this moment Cullen made his entrance from the kitchen and lovingly dragged a length of warm, damp tongue across my hand. The American leapt in alarm.

"God damn!" he shouted. "What in the name of hell's fire is that thing. Boy, you've only been here a year and they've got you as nutty as the rest of them!"

He backed hurriedly to the door and, rain or no rain, scurried through it.

I lingered on in Reception and wondered whether to accept his description as an accolade, or whether, in spite of my efforts, I still had some way to go before being fully accepted by the local population as one of themselves.